Thematic Catalog of a Manuscript Collection
of Eighteenth-Century
Italian Instrumental Music

IN THE UNIVERSITY OF CALIFORNIA, BERKELEY
MUSIC LIBRARY

Thematic Catalog of a Manuscript Collection of Eighteenth-Century Italian Instrumental Music

IN THE UNIVERSITY OF CALIFORNIA, BERKELEY

MUSIC LIBRARY

by Vincent Duckles and Minnie Elmer

WITH THE ASSISTANCE OF PIERLUIGI PETROBELLI

FOREWORD BY DAVID D. BOYDEN

UNIVERSITY OF CALIFORNIA PRESS

BERKELEY AND LOS ANGELES 1963

UNIVERSITY OF CALIFORNIA PRESS
BERKELEY AND LOS ANGELES, CALIFORNIA

CAMBRIDGE UNIVERSITY PRESS
LONDON, ENGLAND

FOREWORD

Those who have tried to hack their way through the thick, forbidding underbrush of the manuscripts, editions, and catalogs of Tartini's music will particularly appreciate the important milestone that the publication of the present catalog represents. The catalog does not pretend to include all the works of Tartini. It describes the contents of a specific collection at Berkeley, which represents not only Tartini's works but also those of a number of composers emanating from his "School of Nations" in Padua, including some hitherto unknown. A central feature of the catalog is, of course, the thematic incipits of the movements of each work concerned.

Naturally, this catalog would have been impossible without the earlier work of others, notably the Dounias catalog of Tartini's concertos (1935) and the recent Brainard catalog of all the sonatas (1959), unfortunately still unpublished. The catalog of the Berkeley collection uses the results of such previous works, amplifying them where necessary. Perhaps the Berkeley catalog will serve to stimulate the publication of similar catalogs of other large collections, especially those in Padua, Paris, and Marburg. Eventually, a complete catalog of the works of Tartini should follow and, let us hope, of others represented in the Berkeley collection. The most important result of all, the publication of accurate editions of individual works, should also be hastened by the present catalog.

The publication of a work of this character and magnitude does not happen of itself. There are generally three basic conditions which must act in concert to produce it. These are a sufficiently important collection to warrant publication; the presence of gifted workers whose devotion to scholarship is matched by specialized knowledge and a fierce passion for undeviating accuracy; and, finally, the will, money, and facilities to publish the results. Sometimes there are, additionally, unexpected vistas of human interest in such undertakings that lend a certain élan or even romantic glow to what is supposedly the drabness of meticulous scholarship.

The Berkeley collection clearly fulfills the first of the conditions just mentioned. Until the collection was acquired by the University of California in 1958, it had been in private hands for upwards of two centuries and was quite unknown to the world of music. It turns out to be one of the richest collections of Tartini manuscripts -- in this respect, to be ranked with those at Padua, Paris, and Marburg. In addition, the Berkeley collection contains far more than the manuscripts of Tartini. However, this point and the extent and richness of the collection need not be pursued here, since a detailed description of the collection is given elsewhere in this catalog.

The second and third of our conditions, basic to publishing the catalog, have also -- needless to say -- been present at Berkeley. The human forces behind the catalog have been Vincent Duckles, Minnie Elmer, and, in its last stages, Pierluigi Petrobelli. Professor Duckles, who found the collection in Italy (as I shall relate presently), had a special interest in the catalog, not only for this reason but also because the publication of a catalog naturally suggested itself to him as head of the Music Library at Berkeley. Miss Elmer, who has long been interested in Tartini, supplied a large part of the sinews of the research involved. In the last year of work, Pierluigi Petrobelli came especially to Berkeley from

Padua to work on the project, and helped greatly through his specialized knowledge of manuscripts and editions contained in Padua and other large European
libraries. The last link in the chain of factors essential to the successful com-
pletion of the published catalog was furnished by the University of California
Press and its officials, together with those of the Music Department.

Finally, since one is not often a party to the acquisition of a collection of such
importance, I cannot refrain from mentioning my own role in the purchase of this
collection and the excitement I experienced in the process. The initial impulse
for acquiring the Berkeley collection came from the lucky juxtaposition of two
American musicologists in Göttingen during 1957-8: Professor Duckles, Fulbright
research fellow during that year, and Paul Brainard, an American who was writing a doctoral dissertation on Tartini's sonatas. In the course of his research,
Brainard came across this collection, the importance of which he mentioned to
Duckles, who lost no time in relaying this information to me, at that time chair-
man of the Music Department at Berkeley. Happily, I was able to convince the
University authorities of the great importance of the collection, and, as a con-
sequence, its purchase followed shortly thereafter. When the collection arrived
in Berkeley, I experienced the special proprietary interest that only the collector
knows; and on examining its contents, I was able to identify a manuscript treatise included in the collection as the long-lost Italian manuscript of Tartini's
Traité des Agrémens. Although I discovered afterwards that Paul Brainard had,
unknown to me, identified it earlier, I basked for some time in the initial glow
of discovery. I later published a specialized description of this treatise in the
Musical Quarterly (July, 1960), and was instrumental in seeing that the original
Italian version of this treatise was incorporated in Dr. Erwin Jacobi's edition of
the Traité, then in course of publication in French, German, and English. By a
curious quirk of fate, another and more complete version of the Italian manuscript was discovered in Venice about the same time by Pierluigi Petrobelli, and
this was the manuscript that Dr. Jacobi finally used for his edition.

Thus the Berkeley collection represents different interests to various persons,
and the ramification of its uses is suggested by what I have already said. We
hope that the present catalog will widen the usefulness of the collection still
further, serving the cause of scholarship and music throughout the world.

David D. Boyden
Oxford, England
March 23, 1963

ACKNOWLEDGMENTS

The preparation of a catalog of this nature could not have been accomplished without the help of many individuals. Paul Brainard is entitled to first mention since it was he who became aware of the collection in the course of his Tartini research at Göttingen and brought it to the attention of the Head of the Music Library at Berkeley. David Boyden, Professor of Music, and Donald Coney, University Librarian, gave the catalog project their support from its beginnings. To Jan La Rue and to Claudio Sartori we are indebted for checking the unknown names in the collection against their files. Gloria Feldman has given us the results of her work on the composer, Paolo Alberghi, conducted as part of her graduate studies at Berkeley, and Sylvia Kramer, another graduate student, made valuable preliminary studies of the watermarks and of the music of Domenico Dall'Oglio. The first steps toward a thematic catalog of the collection were taken in the Spring of 1959 by the members of the graduate seminar, Music 200B, all of whom deserve credit for the final result. Finally, a special word of acknowledgment is due to the two members of the Music Library staff at Berkeley who were responsible for handling some of the most difficult technical details involved in the publication: to Mala Werness who made the thematic incipits, and to Esther Sanematsu who prepared the typescript and organized the final copy.

CONTENTS

INTRODUCTION

HISTORICAL BACKGROUND AND PROVENANCE.

The two main streams which carried Italian musical influences throughout Europe during the late 18th century flowed from opera and from instrumental music. The first had traditionally been associated with southern Italy, with the Neapolitan school of Alessandro Scarlatti and his successors; the second derived chiefly from the north, its initial impetus coming from Bologna in the latter half of the 17th century, spreading to Venice and to Padua. Violinists from all over Europe came to Padua to learn their trade, attracted by the name of the musician whom Sir John Hawkins described as "the last great improver of the practice of the violin," Giuseppe Tartini. Under his influence a new school of violin performance was developed, known as "The School of the Nations" in recognition of the varied national backgrounds of its adherents. The phrase implied not so much an actual institution as a symbol of authority in violin technique and composition. Although one of the leading exponents of the violin as a solo instrument, Tartini did not gain his reputation by traveling as a virtuoso through the various European music centers. Outwardly, at least, his career was that of a quiet, provincial church musician. Except for a period of two years in Prague, he devoted himself for more than forty years to his duties at the Basilica of St. Anthony, playing, teaching, composing and writing the treatises that carried his fame throughout the musical world of his time. Some of his music was printed, but only a small proportion of the total output; most of it survives in manuscript.

Northern Italy, by the second half of the 18th century, was no longer a center of music printing and publishing. The tradition of Petrucci, Antico and Giunta had long since been broken. There were a few publishers such as Antonio Zatta who issued instrumental music from time to time along with general literature, but the leading music publishing houses were located in London, Paris or Amsterdam. This did not mean that the Italian composers were any less productive than they had been in the past. On the contrary, their productivity so far outran the capacities of the press that not even the combined resources of a Welcker, a Le Clerc and a Witvogel could handle it. Music was circulated to a large extent in manuscript copies. The copyist, in fact, was an indispensable figure in the musical economy of the time; every musical establishment of any importance maintained its own "scriptorium." In this the Cappella Antoniana was no exception. But the archive of manuscripts prepared for the use of Tartini and his colleagues has been widely dispersed in the past 200 years. Some remained in Padua, but it is still unclear just how the Tartini manuscripts were deposited in the institution to which the composer was attached. Other segments of the original repertoire, including many Tartini autographs, have found their way into the libraries in Paris, Vienna and Marburg. Still other units have traveled even greater distances from their original location. The purpose of the present catalog is to direct the attention of scholars to a group of manuscripts recently acquired by the Music Library of the University of California at Berkeley, a collection which appears to be the largest single body of works of the Tartini school preserved intact from the 18th century to the present day.

The Berkeley collection comprises some 990 manuscripts containing works by 82 different composers. These works, counted individually, come to a total of 1,062 compositions. There are 75 additional manuscripts containing anonymous works, embellished variants from slow movements of concertos and sonatas, dance music and music for social occasions. The ensemble music, consisting of trio sonatas, quartets and concertos, is preserved in parts. The solo violin sonatas, of which there are approximately 400 examples, appear in a score arrangement, that is, the solo is given with its accompanying bass line in the same system. The composers found in the collection extend from Corelli to Boccherini. Actually the time span is considerably more concentrated than these two names suggest. Corelli is represented only by a manuscript copy of his violin sonatas, Opus 5 (1700) a work which can be considered basic to any library of string music whether of the 18th or of the 20th century. The chronological center of gravity falls within the last quarter of the 18th century, in the works of such musicians as Campioni, Nardini, Pugnani and Helendaal. Two composers, one well known, the other almost completely unknown, serve as the supporting columns for the structure of the library. The well known figure is Tartini himself with 234 works; his little known compatriot is Michele Stratico, who accounts for no less than 283. Together these two musicians are responsible for a little under half of the total number of compositions preserved. Among the few bits of information we have concerning Stratico is the fact that he was a pupil of Tartini. So, also, were at least twelve other musicians represented in the manuscripts at Berkeley: Alberghi, Bini, Ferrari, Fracassini, Helendaal, Holzbogen, Manfredi, Morigi, Nardini, Nazari, Dall'Oglio and Touchemoulin. This in itself would suggest a close connection between these manuscripts and the school of violinist-composers centered at Padua, but even more direct evidence of such connection has been brought to light from a study of the handwritings involved. Two hands in the collection have been identified as the work of violinists employed in the orchestra at Il Santo during Tartini's lifetime. (1)

The international character of the collection is apparent from the first glance. We find musicians of French extraction such as Touchemoulin and Le Chevalier de Saint-Georges, the Belgian, Pierre van Maldere, the Swiss, Kaspar Fritz, the Dutchman, Helendaal, the Germans, Sterkel, Holzbogen and Hoffmeister, and a large contingent of Bohemians (or Czechs) Benda, Kozeluh, Myslivecek, Wanhal, Stamitz and Wodiczka. Haydn is represented by 48 string quartets, extending as far as his Opus 74 and including his Seven Last Words, Mozart, by three late quartets: K.575, K.589 and K.590. One of the most intriguing features of the collection is the presence of substantial lists of works by composers who are obviously skilled craftsmen, if not more, but almost completely unmentioned in the annals of music history. Michele Stratico is the most striking case in point, but one could add other names such as Paolo Alberghi of Faenza, for whom we now have 17 trio sonatas, 11 solo sonatas and 18 concertos, or Domenico Dall'Oglio, who is represented by 22 solo violin sonatas and 17 concertos.

The music is dominated by the three instrumental forms current throughout the 18th century, the trio sonata, the solo sonata, and the concerto. Numerically the sonata for violin and bass is most prominent, with 401 examples, 266 of which are credited to the principal composers, Tartini and Stratico. Next comes the violin concerto with 253 examples, and finally the trio sonata of which there are 237. There remain groups of about 40 duos and 110 or more string quartets, many of the latter designated as "sinfonia a 4." The symphony in the early Classic sense occupies a comparatively small place in this repertoire. The orchestral works, including concertos, are mainly scored for the string group, although there are a few instances in which oboes and horns are required. The concerto parts are almost invariably reduced to the minimum complement, that is, one part for each instrument. There are few ripieno parts, and rarely is more than one part supplied for the violoncello and continuo combined. If these parts were intended for performance use, the ensemble would be a small one involving at most two instruments per stand. There is evidence that the music was occasionally performed with such reduced forces, particularly in private circumstances. A concerto could be transformed into a sonata a tre or a quattro by employing the obbligato parts only. This kind of performance practice is the same

(1) See p. 4-6 for further discussion of this matter.

as that employed by Abate Vincenzo Rota in his transcriptions of Tartini's concertos. The resulting pieces were appropriately called _metamorfosi_, and we have a note in Fanzago's eulogy to the effect that Tartini approved of this practice.

> "Questo rarissimo ingegno ... ha ridotti maravigliosamente per diporto trentasei Conserti del N.A. in sonate a tre, ed a quattro parti obbligate, che intitolò Metamorfosi fedelissime, con tanta soddisfazione del Tartini ..." (1)

The core of Tartini's innovations as a teacher of violin playing is to be found in his approach to ornamentation. His practice was embodied in a treatise which until 1960 was known only in a French translation by P. Denis published in Paris in 1771 under the title, Traité des Agrémens. In July 1960, David Boyden published in the Musical Quarterly (p. 315-328) a description of the sole theoretical work found among the Berkeley manuscripts, a treatise which was in fact the missing Italian text of Tartini's celebrated work. In April of the following year Erwin R. Jacobi described in the same journal (p. 207-223) a second copy of the Italian text in a manuscript in the Conservatorio di Musica "Benedetto Marcello" in Venice. Without going into the vexing question as to which of these manuscripts has the greater authority, it is sufficient to point out that the presence of the treatise among the manuscripts at Berkeley adds further weight to the assumption that these materials are closely connected with Tartini's center of teaching and performance. In addition to the treatise there is a group of 29 manuscripts containing ornamented variants for 267 melodies taken from the slow movements of sonatas and concertos. Most of these give the original, unadorned melody in parallel alignment with one or more elaborated lines. By far the largest number of these demonstrations of embellishment technique are based on movements from Tartini's works; 84 of his concertos and 26 sonata movements are represented. It has been demonstrated that the techniques employed here are directly related to the precepts given in Tartini's treatise. (2)

It is easier to demonstrate the connection between the Berkeley manuscripts and Padua than it is to trace their provenance. One can assume from a study of the handwritings, the watermarks and the repertoire, that the collection was assembled over a limited period of time and for a particular purpose. It has remained substantially in one piece since the end of the 18th century, but its history over the intervening years has not been fully clarified. Some important facts have come to light, however. There is a reference to what may be the collection under consideration in the autobiography of Antonio Bonaventura Sberti, preserved in a manuscript copy in the Biblioteca Civica in Padua. Sberti was an amateur musician and a member of Tartini's circle. In the same autobiography he claims to have furnished Fanzago with the main body of information for the latter's funeral oration. Sberti mentions in his memoirs, dated 1814, that he gave to a certain Giacomo Ziliotto, a _violone_ player of Padua, a collection of music in two cases, which contained:

> ... "tutte le Opere del Corelli, grande numero di Concerti, con Suonate a solo Violino e Basso del Tartini, e del Sig(nor) Michele Stratico, insigne alunno del gran Tartini, oltre due sacchi di Sinfonie, Duetti, etc. di ottimi scrittori di musica." (3)

(1) Fanzago, Francesco: Orazione ... delle Lodi di Giuseppe Tartini. Padova, 1770. Appendice: Compendio della vita di G. T. p. 48.
(2) cf. Elmer, Minnie. Tartini's improvised ornamentation, as illustrated by manuscripts from the Berkeley collection of eighteenth century Italian instrumental music. Unpublished thesis, Univ. of Calif., 1962.
(3) Padova. Biblioteca del Museo Civico, Ms. B.P. 1749/V.

The mention of a large number of instrumental works by Stratico, a composer who is represented, in quantity, in no other known collection, suggests that Sberti may have had the Berkeley manuscripts in his possession at the time. He does not indicate when the collection was given to Ziliotto. We know that it was some time prior to 1814, and the context of Sberti's remarks suggests that the transfer took place before the end of the 18th century.

About 1950 the collection in its present state was purchased by a private collector from the Stecchini family of Bassano del Grappa, not far north of Padua. With the music manuscripts came a large collection of books and family papers principally of the 18th century. The records do not indicate when the music became part of the Stecchini archives, or to what use it was put while in the family's possession. None of the Stecchinis seems to have been active in musical affairs, and from the state of the collection it can be assumed that it was stored unused over a long period of time. To this fortunate circumstance we probably owe the excellent condition of the manuscripts, and the fact that few of the parts have been lost or detached from their respective sets. In the Fall of 1957 the collection was offered for sale, and in the Spring of the following year it was acquired by the University of California Music Library at Berkeley.

A further chapter in the acquisition narrative can be added as a result of Miss Elmer's visit to Italy in 1960/61. Armed with the few facts available to us at that time, she was able to get in touch with the collector who had purchased the Stecchini archive and secure from him a few additional items which had become separated from the rest of the music. Most important of these was the unique copy of Peter Welcker's printing of six sonatas by Michele Stratico, which appeared in London about 1763. Oddly enough, no copy of this work seems to have found its way into any library in England or elsewhere. (1)

HANDWRITINGS AND THEIR RELATIONSHIPS TO OTHER TARTINI COLLECTIONS.

One of the most striking facts about the collection, at a first superficial examination, is the prominence of two handwritings throughout. These two handwritings have been designated as A and B. Hand A is responsible for copies of 156 works of Tartini, for all but two of the Stratico copies, for a large percentage of works by other composers of the Tartini circle, for a number of embellished versions of Tartini's slow movements, and for several anonymous pieces. Copies in Hand A comprise well over half the sonatas, trio sonatas and concertos of the collection, a total of 670 works.

While the amount of music in Hand B is approximately equal in quantity to that in Hand A, it differs significantly in content. Hand B is the copyist of a large body of dance music, including minuets, marches, and other music for social occasions. Aside from manuscripts containing this kind of music, Hand B appears as principal copyist for about sixty works only. However there are additions by Hand B on many sets of parts written in other hands. These additions consist of dynamic markings, trills, and in concertos, of written-out cadenzas -- in other words, additions to pre-existing copies apparently made for performance purposes. Furthermore, as well as making corrections in the musical text, Hand B has added titles when these are lacking in the hands of the original copyists, and for some of the Tartini and Stratico manuscripts, has placed in the upper left corner the abbreviation No: followed by a numeral.

Two thematic catalogs of Tartini's works accompanied the collection when it was acquired by the University of California. One is in Hand A, the other in Hand B. The second includes sonatas and concertos of Stratico as well as works of Tartini. Neither index corresponds precisely to the collection as it now exists: the catalog in Hand A gives themes for 105 concertos and 82 sonatas by Tartini, but

(1) See p.403.

nine of the concertos and six of the sonatas so listed are missing from the collection itself. The briefer catalog in Hand B contains themes for five of the same missing works. However, all the Stratico works are present as separate scores or sets of parts, and the numbers written by Hand B as additions to the title pages of individual works of both composers correspond to the numbers assigned to the same works in the thematic catalog in Hand B. This thematic catalog lists themes for 56 concertos and 50 sonatas of Tartini, and for 18 concertos and 27 sonatas by Stratico. After each group of works there is a blank leaf, as though the compiler had intended to make further additions. The numbers written on the title pages of Stratico sonatas continue through 32. The thematic catalog in Hand B is therefore incomplete, but it is clear that a portion of the collection was assembled, corrected, numbered, and indexed by Hand B, and that the copies so treated were written prior to or coincident with the compilation of the Hand B catalog, which forms an index to a portion of the collection.

Of the various handwritings that appear as the original copyists in manuscripts numbered and listed by Hand B, it has been possible to establish the identity of at least two through a study of the autograph petitions kept in the Archivio Antico della Veneranda Arca del Santo, the depository of the records of the administrative body of the Basilica of St. Anthony in Padua. Hand C is the handwriting of Francesco Melato, active as a violinist in the musical chapel of St. Anthony's from 1740 to 1768, and from about 1750 as principal copyist for the maestro di cappella, Vallotti. Hand D is the handwriting of Bernardino de Zotti, also a violinist in the same institution from 1721 to 1777, the year of his death. Less certain is the identification of Hand I of the Berkeley collection with the hand of Giovanni de Zotti, Bernardino's nephew, who entered the chapel as violinist in 1765. Hand L appears to be identical with the handwriting appearing on a petition by another violinist, Giuseppe Priuli (not necessarily autograph, since Priuli's petitions are in a variety of handwritings) presented on December 29, 1739. These manuscripts of the Berkeley collection, and of the smaller nucleus indexed by Hand B, therefore must have originated in Padua.

There are reasons to assume that Hand A, the principal coypist of the Berkeley collection, was also connected with the Tartini circle. Manuscript IX. 3956 in the library of the Gesellschaft der Musikfreunde in Vienna is a copy of a collection of sonatas for violin and bass and for solo violin in Tartini's autograph. (1) The main handwriting of the Vienna copy is that of Giulio Meneghini, Tartini's pupil and successor at St. Anthony's in Padua, active there from 1756. But in addition to Meneghini's hand, Hand A of the Berkeley collection appears as the copyist of the fifth fascicle of the manuscript. Further associations between Hand A and the Tartini group are evident in manuscripts in the musical archives of St. Anthony's. In a set of parts for Tartini concerto D.22 (2) the violino principale, violino primo and secondo obbligato, and a viola part are in Meneghini's hand. Another viola part and a bass part are in the hand of Bernardino de Zotti (Hand D of the Berkeley collection), but there are two copies of each of the violino ripieno parts in Hand A. A set of parts for Tartini concerto D.30 (3) offers conclusive proof of an association between Hand A and Meneghini, for the violino principale and obbligato parts are in Hand A, but with titles and tempo designations in Meneghini's hand. A viola part begins in Meneghini's hand, but is completed in Hand A.

Another link between Hand A and Meneghini appears in works of Michele Stratico, preserved in the Biblioteca Marciana in Venice. A set of quartets dated 1796 (4) has a violino primo part in Hand A, but title page, viola and bass parts in Meneghini's writing. Sixteen anonymous sonatas, also in the Marciana (5) are copies

(1) Cappella Antoniana, Ms.D.VI. 1888, fasc. 1.
(2) Cappella Antoniana, Ms.D.VI. 1892:106.
(3) Cappella Antoniana, Ms.D.VI. 1902:89.
(4) Biblioteca Marciana, Ms. It. IV. 1521 (11238)
(5) Biblioteca Marciana, Ms. It. IV. 1252 (11066)

of sonatas attributed to Stratico in the Berkeley collection. The volume of sona-
tas in the Marciana is in Hand A, with annotations in code in Meneghini's hand.
This association between Meneghini and Hand A and between Meneghini and
Stratico again place both copyist and composer as members of the Tartini group.

In some respects, Meneghini's relationship to the collections of Tartini manuscripts in the libraries at St. Anthony's and at the Paris Conservatoire is similar to that of Hand B in the Berkeley collection. Meneghini appears as copyist
of some of the Padua manuscripts, as supplier of missing parts in many of the
concertos, and as the originator of annotations in code, which, together with
titles, thematic incipits, tempo and part designations, appear on many works
copied in other hands. In the Paris collection, there are similar additions to
title pages, and occasionally the note "originale," also in Meneghini's hand.
A thematic catalog in the same handwriting in the Paris collection lists 43 sonatas and 85 concertos by Tartini. Presumably this catalog must have been
written in 1797, the year of the French occupation of Padua, for a note at the
end of the last page refers to "cittadino" Pagnini and "commissario" Berthollet.

There is no trace of Meneghini's handwriting in any of the Berkeley manuscripts,
and it therefore seems fairly certain that none of these were part of the legacy
that passed through Meneghini's hands. (1)   Hand B's activity, comparable in
kind to Meneghini's, may have taken place at an earlier date. Judging by the
slender evidence afforded by a few dated manuscripts in the dance music group,
Hand B seems to have been active between 1761 and 1774. It is possible,
therefore, that the assembling of the core of the Berkeley collection as anno-
tated by Hand B may have taken place before Tartini's death.

Other handwritings of the Berkeley collection, although not identified as individuals, draw the lines of relationship of the Berkeley manuscripts to other collections still closer.   In addition to Hands A, C and D, Hands E, G, N and I
are common to the Berkeley collection and to the collection at St. Anthony's as
copyists of Tartini's works. Hand R appears in Dall'Oglio works in Berkeley,
but as a copyist of Tartini sonatas in the library of the Paris Conservatoire. The
small collection of music manuscripts at the Biblioteca Comunale in Ancona includes a second thematic catalog in Hand A, containing incipits for concertos
and sonatas of both Tartini and Stratico. Although there are no works by Stratico
in the Ancona collection, there are copies of Tartini's music in Hands A and I,
and in Hand C, that of Francesco Melato.

The fragment that has been identified as Tartini's autograph (It. 1016) is a final
bit of evidence of an association between the Berkeley collection and the Tartini school. It consists of two leaves, one showing the manner of playing the
arpeggios in the first Allegro of Concerto D. 63, the other an embellished version of the slow movement of the same concerto. In the autograph score at
Padua, (2) the arpeggios of the first movement are written out in full. They are
abbreviated in the copy of the solo part (It. 891) of the Berkeley set. It is con-
ceivable that the Tartini autograph may have been \sketched by the composer as
a supplement to the Berkeley copy of the concerto.

On the basis of this partial survey of other collections of Tartini copies, it has
been established that Hand A and the other copyists discussed above worked at
Padua, and that the main body of the Berkeley manuscripts originated there.
Other segments of the collection are probably from other localities. Many of
the Alberghi copies are in handwritings that appear only in Alberghi manuscripts,
The Haydn and Mozart quartets, also in handwritings not found elsewhere in the
collection, may have been imported from other centers, and added to the collection after its main part had been assembled.

(1) See Brainard, Paul. Die Violinsonaten Giuseppe Tartinis. p. 78ff.
(2) Cappella Antoniana, Ms. Autograph D. VII. 1902:66B.

EXAMPLES OF HANDWRITINGS

EXAMPLES OF HANDWRITINGS

Hand B[1]

Hand C

Hand D

WATERMARKS

Most of the papers of the Berkeley collection bear watermarks containing one form or another of the three halfmoons which are typical of paper produced in the Venetian region during the 18th century; and countermarks consisting of letters, elementary designs, or both. There has been no attempt to identify incomplete watermarks, and if the full folio is not present in a particular manuscript, the watermark has been designated "unclear." Even with this limitation, the total number of watermarks that can easily be distinguished is 106. However, many of these occur in isolated examples, and about a third of the collection is copied on twelve different kinds of paper. Watermark 3, consisting of three halfmoons and a comet, is the design that is found most frequently. It appears in over sixty manuscripts. Watermarks 4, 16, and 63A appear in over forty each, watermarks 5, 53, 63 and 64 in over thirty each, and watermarks 29, 31, 50 and 77 in over twenty each.

Throughout, the watermark information supplements and strengthens the evidence of the handwritings. The Alberghi manuscripts whose handwritings are different from the handwritings of the rest of the collection also display different watermarks. The same watermarks (particularly 7 and 8) are found in manuscripts preserved in the musical archives of the Duomo at Faenza, the center of Alberghi's activity. (1) Certain groups of manuscripts, such as the Tartini trio sonatas copied in Hand A, and the Campioni and Stratico trios in the same hand, appear to have been prepared as groups, for the same watermarks occur repeatedly in manuscripts of each series.

It has not been possible to compare the watermarks of the Berkeley manuscripts with those of the collection at St. Anthony's. However, Brainard has illustrated two watermarks found in Tartini ·autographs in Padua. (2) One of these corresponds to Berkeley watermark 62, which appears in fourteen of the Berkeley manuscripts, ten of them containing music by Tartini, the others works of Sammartini and Stratico. These copies are in Hands A, A^1, B, B^1, B^2 and H^1. The Berkeley autograph has watermark 73, found in fifteen other manuscripts of the collection. These are copies of works of Tartini in Hands B^2 and I, of Dall'Oglio in Hand R, and of Alberghi, Bini, Stratico and others in Hands A, A^2 and B. Thus both manuscripts and handwritings can be dated, at least to the extent of saying that paper used by these copyists was in existence before 1770.

Similarly, copies in the handwritings of Francesco Melato and Bernardino De Zotti can be dated as written on paper produced before 1768 and 1777 respectively. Papers with the same watermarks as those that appear in copies by Melato occur in manuscripts written by Hands A, A^1, B, B^2, K and N. Watermarks comparable to those of the De Zotti manuscripts are found only in copies in Hand A.

The dated manuscripts of the Berkeley collection fall within the same period. There is only one example of watermark 18, which appears in the Albinoni Balletti, dated 1728 (It. 63). Aside from this, the earliest dates, 1756 and 1759, appear on Alberghi works, with handwritings and watermarks not found elsewhere in the collection. One of the Marcelli manuscripts, dated 1760, is in a handwriting and with a watermark unique to the works of this composer. However, paper with watermark 80, which appears in a Tartini concerto dated 1766 (It. 915) in Hand S, is used for another Tartini copy in Hand A. The concerto which is attributed to both Tartini and Stratico (It. 900) is dated 1768 in the copy in Hand F. Its watermark, 56, appears in twenty-five other manuscripts containing music of Nardini, Dall'Oglio, Sciabra, Gobbis, Tartini and Stratico, all copied by Hands A and B. Watermarks 64 and 69 appear in a collection of six Tartini sonatas (It. 694). In this collection, there is a minuet in Hand F by another composer, dated 1778. Watermark 64 appears in thirty-six manuscripts of Tartini and Stratico in Hands A, B^2 and N; watermark 69 in nineteen manuscripts of

(1) This information was supplied by Gloria Feldman.
(2) See Brainard, Paul. Die Violinsonaten Giuseppe Tartinis. p. 209.

Tartini and Stratico, all in Hand A.

Manuscripts of dance music in Hand B are sometimes dated. Some, which have watermarks corresponding to those of the main body of the collection, furnish additional statistics for the principal handwritings. One minuet is headed <u>1761 30 8bre</u>, and paper with the same watermark (78) is used in three other manuscripts in Hand B, two with music of Ferrari, one with music of Tartini. Watermark 17, which appears in a dance manuscript dated <u>6 9bre del 62</u>, is also found in six manuscripts in Hand A, containing music of Besozzi, Gallo and Tartini. Watermark 31, similarly dated <u>14 gennaio 1774</u>, is found in twenty-two manuscripts in Hand A, with music of Conti, Dall'Oglio and Stratico. The earliest date in any of the dance manuscripts is 1750. The watermark of this copy, watermark 27, appears in ten other manuscripts in Hands A, B and G, with music of Brioschi, Stratico and Tartini.

Several of the descriptions of watermarks given by Bartha and Somfai in their study of the Haydn manuscripts at Esterhazy (1) seem to correspond to some of the watermarks of the Berkeley collection. The dates assigned to these watermarks at Esterhazy range from 1762 to 1790. Watermark 3, the most frequent in the Berkeley collection, is found in a manuscript dated 1776. Watermarks dated in the 1780's and 1790's occur less frequently in the Berkeley collection, and not in any manuscripts in the principal handwritings.

If, as Heawood (2) suggests, stocks of paper with given watermarks were exhausted within a year or two during the late 18th century, the evidence of the watermarks of the Berkeley collection corresponds to that of the handwritings, and leads to the same conclusions. The most important of these are first, that the core of the Berkeley collection, as copied in Hands A, B, C, D, E, F, G, I, N and R, and with them, most 18th century copies of Tartini's works in other locations, all originated in a relatively short space of time, namely, during the last years of Tartini's life and certainly within a decade after his death; second, that their place of origin is in or near Padua; and last, that they represent the work of musicians and copyists associated in one capacity or another with the musical chapel at St. Anthony's.

(1) Bartha, Denes and Laszlo Somfai. <u>Haydn als Opernkapellmeister</u>. Budapest, 1960.
(2) Heawood, Edward. <u>Watermarks, mainly of the 17th and 18th centuries.</u> Hilversum, 1950.

LETTERS, NUMBERS AND PRINCIPAL SYMBOLS OF WATERMARKS

LETTERS

A	WM 12, 16, 32, 69, 76, 85	FAS/G	WM 67
AC	WM 14, 14A	FC	WM 18, 44, 53, 73, 93, 97, 104
ACF	WM 61	FF	WM 3, 3A, 3B, 84, 88, 98
AF	WM 62, 74, 81, 88	FV	WM 39, 40, 54, 87, 106
AFG	WM 2, 91	FV/A	WM 88
AFS	WM 22, 68	G	WM 67
AHF	WM 47	GB	WM 51
AM	WM 43, 101	GF	WM 5, 7, 48, 56
AS	WM 64, 66	GFA	WM 13, 33
AS/A	WM 12, 16, 76	GRA	WM 45
AS/C	WM 1	IMC	WM 57
AS/F	WM 6	M	WM 4, 15, 22, 25, 38
AS/M	WM 4, 15, 38	MA	WM 43, 101
AS/P	WM 17	P	WM 17
AS/Z	WM 78	PCC	WM 31, 36, 58
AZ	WM 72	PM	WM 8
BC	WM 102	PS	WM 99
BF	WM 59	RGA	WM 55
C	WM 9	VA	WM 46
CF	WM 5, 94	VB	WM 21
CSC	WM 42, 49	VC	WM 24, 27, 27A
CZ	WM 20	VL	WM 81
CZF	WM 26	VS	WM 96
CZO	WM 30	VV	WM 25
DF	WM 95	VZ	WM 50, 63, 63A
DV	WM 24	VZZ	WM 75
F	WM 6, 71, 100	Z	WM 78, 79
FA	WM 10, 11, 103	ZA	WM 77, 77A
FAC	WM 9, 28, 29, 35, 60	ZAC	WM 34
FAS/A	WM 69	ZV	WM 82, 86

NUMBERS

1	WM 20
3	WM 62
IV	WM 70

WORDS

COMICI ZUCCHETTI OLIERO	WM 41
REAL	WM 13, 20, 25, 26, 30, 47, 48, 49, 82, 88, 91, 100, 105

SYMBOLS

Baldachin	WM 5, 32, 33, 35, 42, 44, 45, 46, 48, 51, 55, 56, 59, 61, 99
Bird	WM 31, 52
Bow	WM 19, 19A, 34, 43, 63, 63A, 77, 77A, 79, 82, 83, 92
Circle	WM 7, 8, 23, 52, 65
Comet	WM 3, 3A, 98
Cross	WM 27, 27A
Crown	WM 4, 11
Fleur de lys	WM 3, 21, 23, 36
Scroll	WM 10, 21, 24, 37, 38, 60, 80, 89, 90, 95, 102, 104
Shield	WM 5, 6, 9, 22, 25, 34, 47, 54, 68, 81, 84
Spearhead	WM 29, 40, 53, 58
Stars	WM 3B, 5, 47, 68, 89
Trefoil	WM 7, 8, 18, 28, 70, 72, 76, 92, 96, 97
Wheel	WM 2

WATERMARKS IN NUMERICAL ORDER

WM	Description	Date	No. of examples
1	L center 3 halfmoons facing right R center C, lower right corner AS		9
2	L center AFG under wheel R blank		8
3	L center 3 halfmoons facing right R center comet, lower right corner F reversed F under fleur de lys	1776 (Bartha)	63
3A	L center 3 halfmoons facing right R center comet, lower right corner F reversed F		15
3B	L center 3 halfmoons facing right R center large star (incomplete)		1
4	L center 3 halfmoons facing right over M R center crown, lower right corner AS	1766 (dated ms.)	54
5	L center shield with 3 stars R center CF (or GF) under baldachin		12
6	L center small shield with AS R center 3 halfmoons facing right over F reversed		35
7	L blank R center GF in circle under trefoil	1756 (dated ms.)	12
8	L blank R center PM in circle under trefoil		13
9	L incomplete R center shield with FA over C		2
10	L center 3 halfmoons facing right R right of center FA under scroll		1
11	L center 3 halfmoons facing right R center FA under small crown		3
12	L center 3 halfmoons facing right over A R lower right corner AS		11
13	L center GFA R center 3 halfmoons facing left over REAL reversed	1780 (Bartha)	1
14	L lower left corner AC R center 3 halfmoons facing right		13
14A	L center 3 halfmoons facing right R lower right corner AC		24
15	L center 3 halfmoons facing right over M R lower right corner AS		11

WATERMARKS IN NUMERICAL ORDER

WM	Description	Date	No. of examples
16	L center 3 halfmoons facing right R center A, lower right corner AS		50
17	L center 3 halfmoons facing right over P R lower right corner AS	1762 (dated ms.)	6
18	L center 3 halfmoons facing right R lower right corner large FC under trefoil	1728? (dated ms.)	1
19	L off center 3 small halfmoons facing left R center long bow pointing right		17
19A	L off center 3 small halfmoons facing left R center long bow pointing left		10
20	L upper center CZ1 R upper center 3 halfmoons facing right over REAL		5
21	L center scroll R lower right corner VB under fleur de lys		1
22	L center 3 halfmoons facing right over M R center small shield with AFS		11
23	L blank R center fleur de lys in circle		4
24	L upper center DV (or reversed VC) under scroll R center 3 halfmoons facing left		4
25	L center shield with M (or reversed VV) R center 3 halfmoons facing left over REAL	1776 (Bartha)	7
26	L upper center REAL R upper center 3 halfmoons facing right, lower left corner CZF		6
27	L off center VC under cross R blank	1750 (dated ms.)	10
27A	L lower left corner VC under cross R center 3 halfmoons facing left		4
28	L center 3 halfmoons facing right R center FA over C under trefoil		18
29	L center 3 halfmoons facing right R center FA over C under spearhead		32
30	L center CZ over O R center 3 halfmoons facing right over REAL		4
31	L blank R center bird over P over C reversed C	1774 (dated ms.)	22

WATERMARKS IN NUMERICAL ORDER

WM	Description	Date	No. of examples
32	L center 3 halfmoons facing right R center A under baldachin		21
33	L center GFA under baldachin R center 3 halfmoons facing left	1781 (Bartha)	7
34	L center 3 small halfmoons facing left over bow R center shield with ZA over C reversed	1776 (Bartha)	3
35	L center 3 halfmoons facing right R center FA over C under baldachin		7
36	L center fleur de lys over P over C reversed C R center 3 halfmoons facing left		14
37	L center 3 halfmoons facing right R center scroll (incomplete)		4
38	L center 3 halfmoons facing right over M R center AS under large scroll		4
39	L off center FV R blank		7
40	L center FV under spearhead R center 3 halfmoons facing left		4
41	L center COMICI over ZUCCHETTI over OLIERO R blank		4
42	L center 3 small halfmoons facing right R center CS over C under baldachin	1789 (Bartha)	4
43	L center AM (or reversed MA) under bow R center 3 halfmoons facing right	1790 (Bartha)	3
44	L center FC under baldachin R center 3 small halfmoons facing left		1
45	L upper center 3 halfmoons facing right R center G over RA under baldachin	1785 (Bartha)	2
46	L center 3 halfmoons facing right R center VA under baldachin		2
47	L center A over HF over REAL R center shield with 3 stars	1776 (Bartha)	12
48	L center 3 halfmoons facing right over REAL R center GF under baldachin	1778 (Bartha)	2
49	L center 3 halfmoons facing right over REAL R center CS over C	1786 (Bartha)	3

WATERMARKS IN NUMERICAL ORDER

WM	Description	Date	No. of examples
50	L lower left corner VZ R center 3 halfmoons facing left		28
51	L center 3 small halfmoons facing right R center GB under baldachin		5
52	L blank R center bird in circle	1760 (dated ms.)	5
53	L center 3 halfmoons facing right R lower right corner FC under spearhead		37
54	L blank R off center shield with FV		1
55	L center RGA under baldachin R center 3 halfmoons facing left		1
56	L center 3 halfmoons facing right R center GF under baldachin	1768 (dated ms.)	26
57	L blank R upper center IM over C		2
58	L center 3 halfmoons facing right R lower right corner spearhead over P over C reversed C		20
59	L center 3 halfmoons facing right R center BF under baldachin		9
60	L center scroll and crescent R center FA over C under scroll		3
61	L center A over CF under baldachin R center 3 halfmoons facing left		2
62	L center 3 halfmoons facing right R lower right corner AF3	before 1770 (Brainard)	14
63	L center 3 halfmoons facing left R center bow, lower right corner VZ		40
63A	L center 3 halfmoons facing right R center bow, lower right corner VZ		49
64	L center 3 halfmoons facing right R lower right corner AS	1778 (dated ms.)	37
65	L center 3 halfmoons facing right R center small circle		5
66	L blank R center AS		2
67	L center 3 halfmoons facing right R center G, lower right corner F over AS		6

WATERMARKS IN NUMERICAL ORDER

WM	Description	Date	No. of examples
68	L center shield with AFS R center shield with 3 stars		20
69	L center 3 halfmoons facing right over A R center F over AS	1778 (dated ms.)	20
70	L center 3 halfmoons facing right R center IV under trefoil		1
71	L center 3 halfmoons facing right R lower right corner F		15
72	L center 3 halfmoons facing right R lower right corner AZ under trefoil		1
73	L center 3 halfmoons facing right R lower right corner small FC	before 1770 (Tartini's death)	16
74	L center 3 halfmoons facing right R lower right corner AF	before 1768 (Melato's death)	3
75	L center 3 halfmoons facing right R lower right corner VZ over Z		6
76	L center AS under trefoil R center 3 halfmoons facing left over A	1777 (Bartha)	9
77	L center 3 halfmoons facing right, lower left corner Z over A R center bow	before 1777 (Di Zotti's death)	13
77A	L center 3 uneven halfmoons facing right, lower left corner Z over A R center bow	before 1768 (Melato's death)	12
78	L lower left corner AS R center 3 halfmoons facing right over Z	1761 (dated ms.)	3
79	L center 3 halfmoons facing right R center bow, lower right corner Z	before 1768 (Melato's death)	7
80	L blank R center scroll (incomplete)	1766 (dated ms.)	2
81	L center small shield with AF (or reversed VL) R blank		1
82	L off center ZV over bow R center 3 halfmoons facing left under REAL reversed		4
83	L center 3 large halfmoons facing right R center short bow		6
84	L center shield with FF R center 3 halfmoons facing left		9

WATERMARKS IN NUMERICAL ORDER

WM	Description	Date	No. of examples
85	L center 3 halfmoons facing right R lower right corner A	before 1777 (Di Zotti's death)	3
86	L center 3 halfmoons facing right R lower right corner ZV		1
87	L blank R off center FV		3
88	L center 3 halfmoons facing right over REAL under AF? R center FV (unclear)		1
89	L center scroll R center star		2
90	L center 3 halfmoons facing right R center scroll (incomplete)		1
91	L center 3 halfmoons facing right over REAL R lower center AFC or AFG	1780 (Bartha)	1
92	L lower left corner trefoil R center small bow	before 1768 (Melato's death)	1
93	L center 3 halfmoons facing right R lower right corner large FC	1762 (Bartha)	1
94	L center 3 halfmoons facing right R lower right corner CF	before 1777 (Di Zotti's death)	1
95	L center 3 halfmoons facing right R center DF under scroll	before 1777 (Di Zotti's death)	1
96	L center 3 halfmoons facing right R lower right corner VS under trefoil		1
97	L center 3 halfmoons facing right R lower right corner small FC under trefoil		1
98	L center 3 halfmoons facing right R center comet, lower right corner FF		16
99	L center PS under baldachin R center 3 halfmoons facing left		1
100	L center REAL R center F		1
101	L center 3 halfmoons facing right R center AM (or reversed MA)		1
102	L center scroll R lower right corner BC		1
103	L center 3 halfmoons facing left over FA R blank (incomplete)		1

WATERMARKS IN NUMERICAL ORDER

WM	Description	Date	No. of examples
104	L center 3 small halfmoons facing right R center FC separated by scroll		1
105	L center REAL R center 3 halfmoons facing right (incomplete)		1
106	L center 3 halfmoons facing right R center large FV	1785 (Bartha)	2

WM3

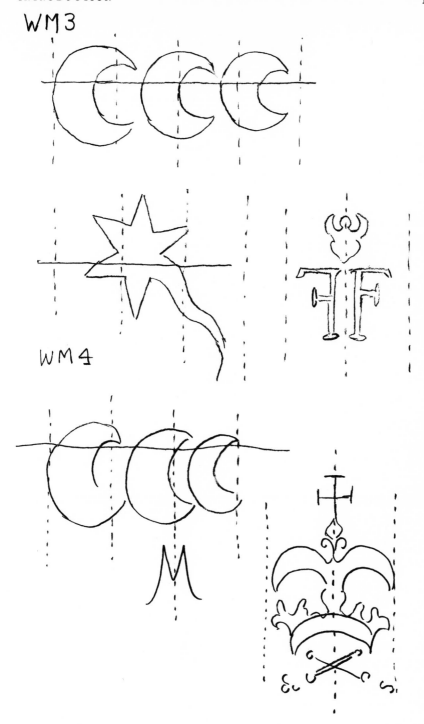

WM4

WM 16

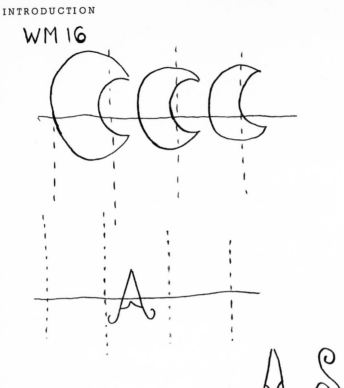

WM62

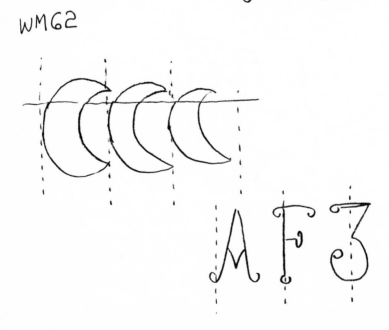

WM 63

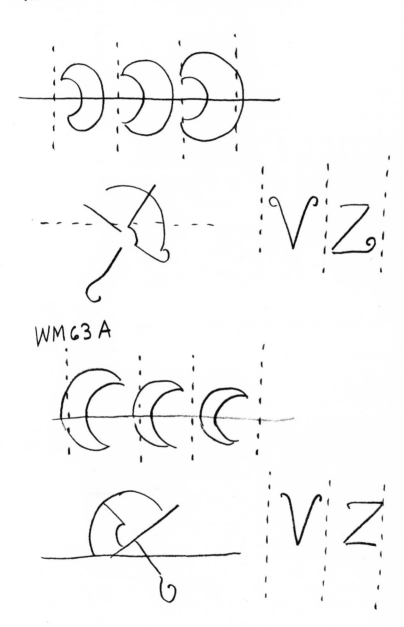

WM 63 A

BIBLIOGRAPHY

CATALOGS.

Breitkopf und Härtel. Catalogo ... Lipsia, 1762-1765, and Supplemento I-XVI. Lipsia, 1766-1787.

The British Union Catalogue of Early Music printed before the year 1801. London, 1957. 2 v.

Catalogo delle Opere Musicali ... Città di Venezia. Parma, n.d. (Bollettino dell'Associazione dei Musicologi Italiani)

Gaspari, Gaetano. Catalogo della Biblioteca del Liceo Musicale del Bologna ... Bologna, 1890-1943. 5 v.

Haas, R. A. Die Estensischen Musikalien; thematischer Verzeichnis ... Regensburg, 1927.

Ecorcheville, J. A. J. Catalogue du Fonds de Musique Ancienne de la Bibliothèque Nationale ... Paris, 1910-1914. 8 v.

La Laurencie, Lionel de. Inventaire Critique du Fonds Blancheton de la Bibliothèque du Conservatoire de Paris ... Paris, 1930-1931. 2 v.

Refardt, Edgar. Thematischer Katalog der Instrumentalmusik des 18. Jahrhunderts in den Handschriften der Universitäts Basel. Bern, 1957.

Riemann, Hugo. Mannheimer Kammermusik des 18. Jahrhundert ... Leipzig, 1914-1915. 2 v. (Denkmäler deutscher Tonkunst, 2. Folge: Denkmäler der Tonkunst in Bayern, 15-16. Jahrg.)

Tebaldini, Giovanni. L'Archivio Musicale della Cappella Antoniana in Padova ... Padova, 1895.

DICTIONARIES.

Choron, A. E. and Fayolle, F. Dictionnaire Historique des Musiciens, Artistes et Amateurs ... Paris, 1810-1811. 2 v.

A Dictionary of Musicians from the Earliest Ages to the Present Time. London, 1824. 2 v.

Dizionario Ricordi della Musica e dei Musicisti. Milano, 1959.

Eitner, Robert. Biographisch-bibliographisches Quellen-Lexikon der Musiker und Musikgelehrten ... Leipzig, 1900-1904. 10 v.

Fétis, F. J. Biographie Universelle des Musiciens ... Paris, 1866-1870. 8 v.

Gerber, E. L. Historisch-biographisches Lexicon der Tonkunstler ... Leipzig, 1790-1792. 2 v.

Gerber, E. L. Neues historisch-biographisches Lexikon der Tonkunstler ... Leipzig, 1812-1814. 4 v.

Grove, Sir George. Dictionary of Music and Musicians. 5th ed., edited by Eric Blom. London, New York, 1954. 9 v.

Larousse de la Musique ... Paris, 1957. 2 v.

Die Musik im Geschichte und Gegenwart ... Kassell, 1949-1961. 8 v.

Muzicka Enciklopedija. Zagreb, 1958. v.1.

Riemann, Hugo. Musik Lexikon. 12. völlig neubearb. Ausg. in drei Bänden ... Mainz, 1959. Personenteil, 2 v.

Schmidl, Carlo. Dizionario Universale dei Musicisti ... Milano, 1928-1929. 2 v. and Supplemento. Milano, 1938.

HISTORIES OF THE VIOLIN.

Bachmann, A. A. Les Grands Violinistes du Passe. Paris, 1913.
La Laurencie, Lionel de. L'Ecole Française du Violon ... Paris, 1922-1924.
3 v.
Moser, Andreas. Geschichte des Violinspiels. Berlin, 1923.
Straeten, E. S. J. van der. The History of the Violin ... London, 1933. 2 v.
Wasielewski, W. J. von. Die Violine und ihrer Meister, bearb. und erganzt ...
Leipzig, 1927.

PUBLISHERS AND WATERMARKS.

Bartha, Denes and Laszlo Somfai. Haydn als Opernkapellmeister. Budapest,
1950.
Heawood, Edward. Watermarks, mainly of the 17th and 18th centuries. Hil-
versum, 1950.
Humphries, Charles and W. C. Smith. Music publishing in the British Isles...
London, 1954.
La Rue, Jan. "Watermarks and Musicology," in Acta Musicologica, 33:120-
146. April-December 1961.
Sartori, Claudio. Dizionari degli Editori Musicali Italiani ... Firenze, 1958.

SPECIAL STUDIES.

Boyden, D. D. "The Missing Italian Manuscript of Tartini's Traité des Agré-
mens," in Musical Quarterly 46:315-328. July 1960.
Brainard, Paul. Die Violinsonaten Giuseppe Tartinis, Unpublished disserta-
tion, Göttingen, 1959.
Capri, Antonio. Giuseppe Tartini. Milano, 1945.
Clercx, Suzanne. Pierre van Maldere, Virtuose et Maitre des Concerts de
Charles de Lorraine, 1729-1768. Bruxelles, 1948. (Académie Royale de
Belgique. Classe des Beaux-arts. Mémoires)
Dounias, Minos. Die Violinkonzerte Giuseppe Tartinis ... Wolfenbüttel-
Berlin, 1935.
Elmer, Minnie. Tartini's Improvised Ornamentation, as illustrated by Manu-
scripts from the Berkeley Collection ... Unpublished thesis, Univ. of
Calif., 1962.
Giazotto, Remo. Tomaso Albinoni. Milano, 1945.
Hoboken, Anthony van. Joseph Haydn; thematisches bibliographisches Werk-
verzeichnis. Mainz, 1957. v.1.
Jacobi, E. R. "G. F. Nicolai's Manuscript of Tartini's Regole per ben suonar
il Violino," in Musical Quarterly 47:207-223. April 1961.
Jacobi, E. R. Giuseppe Tartini ... Traite des Agrements de la Musique.
Celle and New York, 1961.
Köchel, Ludwig. Chronologisch-thematisches Verzeichnis sämtlicher Tonwerke
Wolfgang Amade Mozarts. 3. Aufl., bearb. von Alfred Einstein. Leipzig,
1937.
Mooser, R. A. "Violonistes-Compositeurs Italiens en Russie au XVIIIe Siècle,
IV," in Rivista Musicale Italiana, 48:219-229. Apr.-June 1946.
Newman, W. S. The Sonata in the Baroque Era. Chapel Hill, 1959.
Pelicelli, N. "Musicisti in Parma nel sec.XVIII," in Note d'Archivio, 11:29-
57, 248-281; 12:27-42, 82-92. Jan.-Mar. 1934 - Mar.-Apr. 1935.
Petrobelli, Pierluigi. "Per l'Edizione Critica di un Concerto Tartiniano (D. 21)"
in Numero Unico per la XIX Settimana Musicale Senese, p.97-128. 22-30
July 1962.
Pfäfflin, Clara. Pietro Nardini ... Plieningen-Stuttgart, 1935.
Pincherle, Marc. Le Monde des Virtuoses. Paris, 1961.
Rouvel, Diether. Zur Geschichte der Musik am Fürstlich Waldeckschen Hofe
zu Arolsen. Regensburg, 1962.

Scharnagl, Augustin. Johann Franz Xaver Sterkel ... Würzburg, 1943.

Torrefranca, Fausto. Le Sinfonie dell'Imbrattacarte (G. B. Sanmartini) Torino, 1915.

Zschinsky-Troxler, E. M. von. Gaetano Pugnani, 1731-1798. Berlin, 1939.

SOURCES.

Bagatella, Antonio. Regole per la Costruzione de' Violini ... Memoria Presentata all' Accademia di Lettere ed Arti di Padova ... 1782. Padova, 1786.

Burney, Charles. Dr. Burney's Musical Tours in Europe, edited by P.A. Scholes. London, New York, 1959. 2 v.

Burney, Charles. A General History of Music from the Earliest Ages to the Present Period. London, 1776-1789. 4 v.

Burney, Charles. The Present State of Music in France and Italy. London, 1771.

Burney, Charles. The Present State of Music in Germany, the Netherlands, and United Provinces. London, 1773.

Cartier, J. B. L'Art du Violon ... 3. éd. revue et corigee. Paris, 1804.

Fanzago, Francesco. Orazione ... delle Lodi di Giuseppe Tartini. Padova, 1770.

Hawkins, Sir John. A General History of the Science and Practice of Music. London, 1776. 5 v.

Murr, C. G. von Journal zur Kunstgeschichte und zur allgemeinen Litteratur. Zweyter Theil. Nürnberg, 1776.

Sberti, A. B. Memorie intorno L'Abate Ant^{o}. Bonaventura D^{r}. Sberti, Padovano, scritte da lui medesimo in 9bre 1814. Padova. Biblioteca Civica. Ms. B.P. 1479/V.

Schubart, C. F. D. Ideen zu einer Ästhetik der Tonkunst. Hrsg. von Ludwig Schubart. Wien, 1806.

CONTENT AND ARRANGEMENT OF ENTRIES

The descriptive details given in each entry are intended not only to identify the individual manuscript, but also to point out the relationship of one manuscript to another. The musical incipit identifies the work, but additional information on kind of paper and handwriting serves in some instances to determine the origin and approximate date of the copy.

TITLES. Titles are transcribed exactly, with line endings indicated, on the theory that the arrangement of the title page may have some bearing either on the source of the copy (particularly if it derives from a printed edition) or on the stage of development of the individual copyist. For example, the group of Tartini sonatas in Handwriting A with caption titles seems to have been copied as a unit, and other groups can be assembled on the basis of slightly differing arrangement in the title and slight variations in the handwriting.

For works in several parts, the part bearing the most complete title has been chosen as the source of title transcription, and the name of the part, as violino primo or basso, is included as part of the title. When the title appears in equal fullness on all parts, preference is given to the violino principale of concertos or the violino primo of trios or quartets.

Because of the great variety in orthography, particularly in personal names, spelling errors have not been indicated, even when they are obvious. Such spellings as Tarini for Tartini, Poulo for Paolo, sonatta for sonata, grolioso for glorioso, are transcribed without comment. All titles have been carefully revised, and with a normal margin for error, it should be assumed that apparent typographical errors are deliberate.

THEMES. Themes are transcribed in eighteenth century style. No attempt has been made to modernize the notation, although obvious errors have occasionally been corrected. The spelling of normal tempo designations has been corrected, unusual ones have been transcribed as written. In the case of incomplete sets of parts, a theme is copied from the highest available part, usually the second violin. Themes for fragmentary compositions, included in the working copy of the catalog in the hope that identification would be possible, have been retained in the final version, in spite of the fact that they are obviously of little value.

Thematic incipits are omitted for the works of well-known composers, particularly when a standard thematic catalog is available. For Haydn, Hoboken numbers, and for Mozart, Köchel numbers are given in lieu of theme.

Tartini's works in sonata and concerto form are assigned the numbers given them by Brainard and Dounias respectively. The themes of the movements have not been copied, but since there are discrepancies in the number and order of movements in different copies of the same work, the tempo designation of each movement is quoted. Measure count is added for the concerto movements, but not for the sonata movements, since this information is available in Brainard. Among the sonatas in the Berkeley collection there are a number of examples of two versions, one with double stops, one without. The note, version with double stops, has been added where applicable. When no note is made, it may be assumed that the copy at hand represents the simpler version.

NUMBERING. The numbers at the left are consecutive for works of a single composer in a single medium. The catalog number appears as the first element of the column at the right of the title transcription and thematic incipit. The catalog number is preceded by the abbreviation It., for Italian manuscript.

DESCRIPTION. The physical description of the manuscript appears under the catalog number. The first element is the number of parts. These are listed by means of English abbreviations: vp for violino principale, v 1 & 2 for violino primo & secondo, vlc for violoncello, bass for basso. The names of instruments other than strings: organ, flute, horn, etc., are written out in English, but a designation for a stringed instrument unusual in the present context is spelled out in Italian, for example, contra basso or violone. Further abbreviations are: obl for obbligato, conc for di concerto, rin for di rinforzo, rip for ripieno.

Following the enumeration of the parts are elements describing the kind of paper. All the manuscripts in the collection are written on hand made paper, as a rule cut from sheets about 45x62 centimeters in dimension. The sheets are usually cut across the longer dimension, the half sheet folded, and the edges left untrimmed. Size of the folded half sheet is given to the nearest half centimeter. Number of staves per page follows size. Music paper seems to have been hand ruled in advance, for the ink with which the staves are drawn is often different from that used in the notation. At the head of one of the fragmentary manuscripts is written:

"Quattro fogli di carta come questa, e quattro fogli piu piccola da otto righe, se non hanno di questa piccola sei fogli compagni."

This note creates the impression that music paper was ruled by the manufacturer or supplier. In any event, the number of staves per page has, like variations in the placement of titles, a definite bearing on the order in which certain manuscripts were copied.

The symbol for watermark is the abbreviation WM: followed by a numeral. After a few preliminary attempts at classification, it was decided to number the watermarks as they appeared. A complete list, an index by letter and symbol, and a few examples appear on pps. 11-21. Watermark information cannot be regarded as definitive, for no distinction is made between slight variations in size and placement of symbols. The clarity of the watermarks depends somewhat on the conditions under which the papers were examined. There are errors in identification, particularly in the early part of the catalog, and only Tartini copies have been thoroughly rechecked for accuracy of watermark information.

The last element in the physical description of the manuscript is a symbol for the handwriting and the color of ink. Handwritings found in Tartini copies are given letters A to Z, with subdivisions, as A^1 A^2 A^3 representing similar hands, or possibly the same hand at different stages of development. Handwritings not found in Tartini copies are assigned double or triple letters, AA to ZZZ, and for these, there has been no attempt at classification. Numbers appearing at the head of title in many of the Tartini and Stratico copies appear to have been added in Hand B. This fact is not indicated, but for two Tartini works in which the number appears to have been part of the original title, the note, Number in Hand J, is included. Terms for the color of ink are limited to black and brown. Since the inks have faded to varying degrees, the information is imprecise. Generally, if the lighter strokes of the pen show a brownish tinge, the ink has been considered brown, and it is called black only if there is no noticeable fading. As with the watermarks, the manuscripts were examined in varying lights, natural and artificial, over a considerable period of time: the color designation may not always be consistent. However, even this subjective information has some bearing on the grouping of the manuscripts; for example, it may be significant that Hand A normally uses brown ink, Hand B black.

NOTES. Under the theme itself are notes concerning the copy, such as source of title if there is no title page, presence of a thematic incipit on the title page, figuration in the bass part, etc., and relationship of a theme or movement to other works by the same composer. When possible, references to bibliographies, dates of publication, or other means of identification for individual works, are included.

ARRANGEMENT. Entries are arranged by composer, and under composer by medium of performance in the order of increasing size of ensemble: solos, sonatas for violin and bass, duos, trios, quartets, concertos. Within these groups, the order is first by title, then by key. For example, in the trio group, sonate a 3 are listed separately from sinfonie a 3 or trios. Concertos are arranged in a single order by key, regardless of size of ensemble or number of parts, except in the case of Stratico, where two concertos for two violins precede the normal five part ensembles, and a group of four part concertos (which may be incomplete) are placed at the end.

This composer is unknown to Eitner and to the compilers of the standard sources
of information on violinists and composers of the late 18th century. His name
appears on several manuscript compositions in the Archivio di S. Petronio in
Bologna.

E flat major

1.   Sonata a Tre / Del Sig:^r Giuseppe Aiudi /

It. 1
v 1 & 2, bass.
23.5x31cm. 10 st.
WM: 1.
Hand A. Black.

ALBERGHI, PAOLO, 1716-1785

The 11 sonatas, 17 trio sonatas, and 18 concertos in the present collection re-
present the largest known concentration of instrumental music by this composer.
Alberghi was born and died in Faenza, where he spent most of his active life as
a musician.   He was violinist in the orchestra of the Duomo from 1733, serving
under his brother, Francesco, who was maestro di cappella from 1737 to 1760.
In 1760 Paolo Alberghi succeeded to the post and held it until his death in 1785.
The only reference to an association with Tartini is Burney's statement (General
History, v.3, p.562) that Alberghi was one of Tartini's pupils.   He is cited
briefly by Van der Straeten (v.2, p.64) as violinist and maestro di cappella at
Faenza, ca.1770, but there is no mention of him in Eitner or any of the standard
reference works.   Four of Alberghi's instrumental works are found in a manuscript collection in the Library of Congress; one of them duplicates a concerto
in the Berkeley collection.   Concordances for trio sonatas It. 22 to It. 31 are found
in a group of 23 trios for 2 flutes and bass in the University of California Music
Library.   Alberghi's sacred vocal music is represented in 32 manuscripts in the
Archives of the Duomo in Faenza.   These and other documents in Faenza have
been used to establish authority for the composer's autograph.

C major

1.   Sonata a Violino, e Basso / Del Sig:^r / Paolo Alberghi /

It. 2
score.
23x31.5cm. 10 st.
WM: 2.
Hand B. Black.

Another copy. Sonata Del Sig:^r Paolo Alberghi / a Violino, e
Basso /

    It. 3
    score.
    23.5x31cm. 10 st.

Incipit on t.p.

    WM: unclear.
    Hand AA. Brown.

2.   Sonata a Violino e Basso / Del / Sig^r Paolo Alberghi /

    It. 4
    score.
    23.5x32cm. 10 st.
    WM: 98.
    Hand B. Black.

D major

3.   Sonata a Violino, e Basso / Del / Sig:^r Paolo Alberghi /

    It. 5
    score.
    23x32cm. 10 st.
    WM: 4.
    Hand A. Black.

E major

4.   Sonata a Violino, e Basso / Del / Sig.^r Paolo Alberghi /

    It. 6
    score.
    23x32cm. 10 st.
    WM: 4.
    Hand A. Brown.

F major

5. Sonata a Violino, e Basso / Del Sig:[r] Paolo Alberghi /

It. 7
score.
23x31cm. 12 st.
WM: unclear.
Hand AA. Black.

Incipit on t. p.

6. Sonata a Violino, e Basso / Del Sig:[r] Paolo Alberghi /

It. 8
score.
23.5x31cm. 12 st.
WM: unclear.
Hand AA. Black.

Incipit on t. p.

G major

7. Sonata a Violino, e Basso / Del / Sig:[r] Paolo Alberghi /

It. 9
score.
23.5x32cm. 10 st.
WM: 98.
Hand B. Black.

8. Sonata a Violino, e Basso / Del / Sig:^{r} Paolo Alberghi /

It. 10
score.
23x32cm. 10 st.
WM: 4.
Hand A. Black.

G minor

9. Sonata à Violino, e Basso / Del / Sig.^{r} Paulo Alberghi /

It. 11
score.
23x32cm. 10 st.
WM: 68.
Hand A^2. Black.

Another copy. Sonatta / A Violino e Basso del Sig:^{r} Pouolo
Alberghi / Di Faenza /

Incipit on t.p.

It. 12
score.
21.5x24cm. 12 st.
WM: 22.
Hand BB. Brown.

10. Sonata a Violino, e Basso / Del Sig:^{r} / Paolo Alberghi /

It. 13
score.
23x32.5cm. 10 st.
WM: 5.
Hand B. Black.

Another copy. Sonata a Violino, e Basso / Del Sig:[r] Paolo
Alberghi /

Incipit on t.p.

It. 14
score.
23x30cm. 12 st.
WM: unclear.
Hand AA. Black.

A major

11. Sonata a Violino, e Basso / Del / Sig.[r] Paolo Alberghi /

It. 15
score.
23x32.5cm. 10 st.
WM: 4.
Hand A. Black.

Trios

B minor

1. N.º 1 / Violino Primo / a: 3: / del: Sig: Paolo: Alberghi: /

It. 16
v 1 & 2, bass.
23x32cm. 10 st.
WM: 6.
Autograph. Black.

Adagio is the same as that of Alberghi: Trio sonata, It. 21.

A minor

2.   N⁰ 2: / Violino Primo / a: 3: / Del Sig Paolo: Alberghi /

It. 17
v 1 & 2, bass.
23x31.5cm. 10 st.
WM: 6.
Autograph. Black.

D major

3.   N⁰ 3: / Violino Primo / a: 3: / Del: Sig Paolo Alberghi /

It. 18
v 1 & 2, bass.
23x32cm. 10 st.
WM: unclear.
Autograph. Black.

A major

4.   N⁰ 4: / Violino Primo / a: 3: / Del: Sig: Paolo: Alberghi /

It. 19
v 1 & 2, bass.
23.5x33cm. 10 st.
WM: 6.
Autograph. Black.

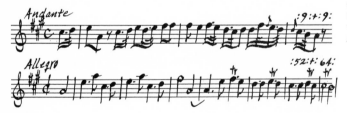

B flat major

5. N° 5 / Violino Primo / a: 3: / Del: Sig: Paolo Alberghi /

It. 20
v 1 & 2, bass.
23x32cm. 10 st.
WM: 6 & unclear.
Autograph &
Hand A. Brown.

D major

6. N° 6: / Violino Primo / a: 3 / Del: Sig Paolo Alberghi /

It. 21
v 1 & 2, bass.
23.5x31.5cm. 10 st.
WM: 6.
Autograph. Brown.

Adagio is the same as that of Alberghi: Trio sonata, It. 16.

C major

7. Basso / Sonata a tre / Del Sig: Paolo Alberghi / Anno 1759 /

It. 22
v 1 & 2, bass.
22x30cm. 10 st.
WM: 7.
Autograph. Brown.

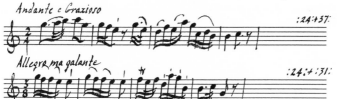

D major

8. Basso / Sonata: a tre / Del: Sig: Paolo Alberghi: / Anno 1759 /

It. 23
v 1 & 2, bass.
22x30.5cm. 10 st.
WM: 7.
Autograph. Black.

9. No. 1. / Basso / Sonata a tre da camera / Del: Sig Paolo
    Alberghi / Anno 1759 /

It. 24
v 1 & 2, bass.
22.5x30cm. 10 st.
WM: 7.
Autograph. Black.

F major

10. Basso / Sonata a tre / Del: Sig Paolo Alberghi / Anno 1759 /

It. 25
v 1 & 2, bass.
22x30.5cm. 10 st.
WM: 7.
Autograph. Black.

On v 1 and bass: V.B.
On v 2: V.B. Teresa Poggi.

G major

11. Basso / Sonata a tre: / Del Sig Paolo Alberghi / Anno 1759 /

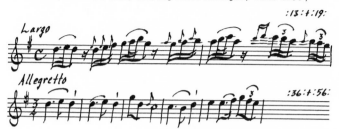

It. 26
v 1 & 2, bass.
22x30.5cm. 10 st.
WM: 7.
Autograph. Black.

B flat major

12. Basso / Sonata: a tre: / Del Sig Paolo Alberghi / Anno 1759 /

It. 27
v 1 & 2, bass.
22x30.5cm. 10 st.
WM: 7.
Autograph. Brown.

On all parts in another hand: V.B.

D major

13. Basso / Terzetto Del Sig Paolo Alberghi /

It. 28
v 1 & 2, bass.
23x31cm. 10 st.
WM: 8.
Hand CC. Black.

G major

14. Terzetto Del Sig Paolo Alberghi /

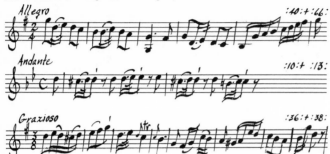

It. 29
v 1 & 2 [bass]
22.5x30.5cm. 10 st.
WM: 8.
Hand CC. Black.

G minor

15. Basso / Terzetto Del Sig Paolo Alberghi /

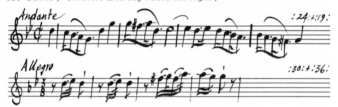

It. 30
v 1 & 2, bass.
23x31cm. 10 st.
WM: 8.
Hand CC. Black.

A minor

16. Basso / Terzetto del Sig Paolo Alberghi /

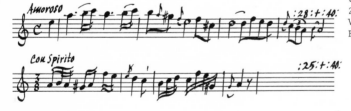

It. 31
v 1 & 2, bass.
22.5x30.5cm. 10 st.
WM: 8.
Hand CC. Black.

F major

17. Trio del Sig: / Paolo Alberghi / Violino Primo /

It. 32
v 1 & 2, bass.
23.5x30.5cm. 10 st.
WM: unclear.
Hand DD. Black.

Concertos

C major

1. Violino Principale / Concerto / Del Sig.[r] Paolo Alberghi /

It. 33
vp, v 1 & 2 obl,
bass.
23.5x31.5cm. 10 st.
WM: 10 & 9.
Hand A. Brown.

Embellished version of Adagio: It. 1005:24.

2.   Concerto del Sig.^r Paolo Alberghi / Faenza 1756 /

It. 34
vp, v 1 & 2 obl,
vla, bass, horn
1 & 2.
22x30.5cm. 10 st.
WM: 7.
Hand GG. Black.
(incipits in Hand
HH)

On t.p.: 4 incipits with superscription: In cambio si
dessiderano li accenati.
Allegro 2 is the same as the Allegro of Tartini Concerto D 6,
with differences in figuration.

Another copy. Violino Principale / Concerto / Del Sig.^r Paolo
Alberghi /

It. 35
vp, v 1 & 2 obl, vla,
bass, horn 1 & 2.
23x32.5cm. 10 st.
WM: 5 & 2.
Hand B. Black.

D major

3.   Violino Principale / Concerto a Cinque del Sig.^r / Paolo
Alberghi / Mastro di Capella in Patria /

It. 36
vp, v 1 & 2 obl, vla,
bass obl, organ
(figured), horn 1 & 2.
22.5x30cm. 10 st.
WM: 8 & 7.
Hand EE. Brown.

Another copy. Violino Principale / Concerto / Del Sig.^r Paolo
Alberghi /

It. 37
vp, v 1 & 2 obl, vla,
vlc obl, horn 1 & 2.
22.5x31cm. 10 st.
WM: 11 & 2.
Hand B. Black.

<u>Another copy</u>. First solo of first allegro only.

It. 38
vp.
fragment. 9 st.
WM: none.
Hand B[3]. Black.

4. Concerto con Violino Obligato / con Strum:[i] / Del Sig:[r] Paolo
    Alberghi / Organo /

It. 39
v 1 obl, v 1 & 2
conc, v 1 & 2 rip,
organ (figured),
trumpet 1 & 2.
22x30cm. 10 st.
WM: 7.
Hand FF. Brown.

5. Violino Principale / Concerto / Del Sig.[r] Paolo Alberghi /

It. 40
vp, v 1 & 2 obl,
vla obl, vlc obl.
22x30cm. 10 st.
WM: 73.
Hand A. Brown.

<u>Name on t. p. crossed out.</u> <u>In another hand:</u> Questo non è
assolutamente del Sig:[r] Alberghi / ma bensi d'uno il quale a
coppiati qualche sentimenti d'altri Concerti / del medemo .
Alberghi é chi ciò dice lo manterà avendo / ancor io   imparato
il contrapunto sotto il medemo .   Alberghi / e sò francam: la
maniera del suo Scrivere /

6.   Violino Principale / Concerto / Del Sig.^r Paolo Alberghi /

It. 41
vp, v 1 & 2 obl,
vla obl, bass.
23.5x32.5cm.10 st.
WM: 98.
Hand B. Black.

Another copy. Violino Principale / Concerto a Cinque obligato /
del / Sig. Paolo Alberghi di / Faenza /

It. 42
vp, v 1 & 2 obl,
vla, bass.
22.5x30.5cm.10 st.
WM: 7.
Hand JJ. Brown.

E major

7.   Violino Principale / Concerto / Del Sig.^r Paolo Alberghi /

It. 43
vp, v 1 & 2 obl,
vla, vlc obl.
22.5x33cm. 10 st.
WM: 3 & 68.
Hand A^2. Brown.

<u>G major</u>

8.   Violino Principale / Concerto / Del Sig.^r Paolo Alberghi /

It. 44
vp, v 1 & 2 obl,
vla, bass.
23x32cm. 10 st.
WM: 5 & 2.
Hand B. Black.

<u>Another copy</u>. Violino Principale / Concerto / Del Sig^r Paolo
Alberghi /

Incipit on t. p.

It. 45
vp, v 1 & 2 obl,
vla, bass.
23x30.2cm. 10 st.
WM: 16.
Hand GG. Brown.

9.   Violino Principale / Concerto / Del Sig.^r Paolo Alberghi /

It. 46
vp [v 1 obl] v 2
obl, vla, vlc obl.
23x32.5cm. 10 st.
WM: 28 & 3.
Hand A^2. Brown.

10. Violino Principale / Concerto con Stromenti Obbligati / del
Signor / Paolo Alberghi / Mastro di Capela in Patria / Faenza /

It. 47
vp, v 1 & 2 conc,
vla, organ (figured),
horn 1 & 2.
22.5x30cm. 10 st.
WM: 8.
Hand EE. Brown.

Another copy. Violino Principale / Concerto / Del Sig.[r] Paolo
Alberghi /

It. 48
vp, v 1 & 2 obl,
vla [bass]
23x31cm. 10 st.
WM: 15 & 14.
Hand A. Black.

11. Violino Principale / Concerto / Del Sig:[r] Paolo Alberghi /

It. 49
vp, v 1 & 2 obl,
vla, bass.
22.5x31cm. 10 st.
WM: unclear.
Hand B. Black.

A major

12. Concerto del Sig.^r Paolo Alberghi / Faentino / Violino Secondo
    Obligato /

It. 50
[vp] v 1 & 2 obl,
vla, vlc.
22x30cm. 10 st.
WM: 8.
Hand HH. Brown.
(parts in other
hands)

Embellished version of Largo: It. 1005:22.

Another copy. Violino Principale / Concerto / Del Sig:^r Paolo
Alberghi /

It. 51
vp, v 1 & 2 obl,
vla, vlc.
23x32cm. 10 st.
WM: 5 & 2.
Hand B. Brown.

13. Violino Principale / Concerto / Del Sig.^r Paolo Alberghi /

It. 52
vp, v 1 & 2 obl,
vla, bass.
23.5x32.5cm.10 st.
WM: 15.
Hand A. Brown.

Another copy. Violino Principale / Concerto / Del Sig:^r Paolo
Alberghi /

It. 53
vp, v 1 & 2 obl,
bass.
23x31cm. 10 st.
WM: unclear.
Hand B. Black.

14. Violino Principale / Concerto a 5 con Violino Principale / Del
    Sig. Paolo Alberghi Mastro di Capella / in Patria / Faenza /

It. 54
vp, v 1 & 2 conc,
vla, organ (figured)
22.5x30.5cm. 10 st.
WM: 7 or 8.
Hand EE. Brown.

Another copy. Violino Principale / Concerto / Del Sig:^r Paolo
Alberghi /

It. 55
vp.
23x32cm. 10 st.
WM: 11.
Hand B. Black.

15. Violino Principale / 1756 / Concerto del Signor Paolo Alberghi
    Faentino /

It. 56
vp, v 1 conc, v 2
obl, vla, vlc obl.
22.5x30cm. 10 st.
WM: 8.
Hand HH. Brown.
(parts in auto-
graph?)

Incipit on t. p.

Another copy. Violino Principale / Concerto / Del Sig:^r Paolo
Alberghi /

It. 57
vp, v 1 & 2 obl,
vla, vlc obl.
23x32.5cm. 10 st.
WM: 5.
Hand B. Black.

16. Concerto a Cinque con Violino Principale del Sig:^r Palo
    Alberghi. Organo /

It. 58

vp, v 1 obl, v 2
conc [vla] organ.
22.5x30.5cm.10 st.
WM: 7 or 8.
Hand CC. Brown.
(parts in auto-
graph?)

On vp: C.N.

Another copy. Violino Principale / Concerto / Del Sig^r Paolo
Alberghi /

It. 59

vp, v 1 & 2 obl,
vla, bass.
23x31.5cm. 10 st.
WM: 11 & 2.
Hand B. Black.

A minor

17. Violino Principale / Concerto a Cinque / Del Sig.^r Paolo
    Alberghi / Mastro di Capella in / Faenza /

It. 60

vp, v 1 & 2 obl,
vla obl, bass
(figured).
22.5x30cm. 10 st.
WM: 8.
Hand EE. Brown.

Another copy. Violino Principale / Concerto / Del Sig:^r Paolo
Alberghi /

It. 61

vp, v 1 & 2 obl,
vla obl, bass.
23x32cm. 10 st.
WM: 5 & 2.
Hand B. Black.

B flat major

18. Violino Principale / Concerto / Del Sig:^r Paolo Alberghi /

It. 62
vp, v 1 & 2 obl,
vla, bass.
23.5x32cm. 10 st.
WM: 98.
Hand B. Black.

Embellished version of Adagio: It. 993:1, It. 1005:26.

For additional concertos in D major and A major, see anonymous works It. 1051
and It. 1053.

[ALBINONI, TOMASO, 1671-1750]

Although given as Baletti del Corelli (1728) on the single Violin I part at Berkeley, these works have been identified with a manuscript set of Balletti a 4 by
Tomaso Albinoni in the Estensische Sammlung of the Kunsthistorisches Museum
in Vienna. (See Robert Haas, Die Estensischen Musikalien. Thematisches Ver-
zeichnis. Regensburg, 1927, p. 165-66.) The Vienna copy contains parts for
Violino Primo, Violino Secondo, Violetta and Basso Continuo. No Balletti a 4 by
Albinoni appear to have been published, nor are these works cited in lists given
by Giazotto in his biography of the composer (Milan, 1945) by Eitner or by MGG.
Three-voice Balletti, published as Op. 3 in 1701, can be found cited in at least
seven editions, from 1703 to 1732, in the British Union Catalogue of Early
Music.
Albinoni was possibly a pupil of Legrenzi and was active as a violinist and composer in Venice. Described as a "dilettante" by his contemporaries, he was
nevertheless a skilled composer, credited with fifty-five operas, cantatas, and
at least nine published sets of instrumental works. Many of the latter are
known in modern performing editions.

[ALBINONI, TOMASO]

1. 1728 / Baletti del Corelli /

It. 63
v 1.
24x31cm. 10 st.
WM: 18.
Hand KK. Brown.

G major

Sonata P.ª

B minor

Sonata 2dª.

D major

Sonata Terza.

A major

Sonata Quarta.

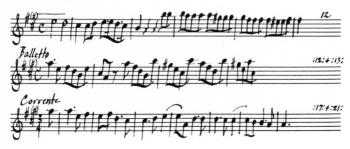

C major

Sonata Quinta.

E minor

Sonata Sesta.

F major

Sonata Settima.

A minor

Sonata Ottava.

B flat major

Sonata Nona.

D minor

Sonata Decima.

E major

Sonata Undecima.

G minor

Sonata Duodecima.

BARBELLA, EMANUELE, 1704?-1777

Violinist-composer active in Naples where he was a member of the orchestras of the Royal Chapel and of the Teatro San Carlo. He is represented by one trio sonata in the Berkeley collection. Among Barbella's teachers were Leonardo Leo and Pasqualino Bini. The latter, a pupil of Tartini, undoubtedly imparted some of the quality of the north-Italian violin school since Burney describes Barbella as a "modest ingenious musician, and true follower of Tartini's principles". (General History of Music, 3, p.570) Violin sonatas, trio sonatas and duos by Barbella were published in London and Paris. An opera, Elmira Generosa, written with Logroscino, was performed in Naples in 1753.

G major

1. Trio / Del Sig.^r Emanuele Barbella / Basso /

It. 64
v 1 & 2, bass.
25x31.5cm. 10 st.
WM: 29.
Hand A. Brown.

Bohemian violinist and composer, and chamber musician to the Crown Prince of Prussia (later Friedrich II).   Solo sonatas for violin and for flute, violin concertos and trio sonatas were published in Berlin and Paris, and considerable instrumental music has been preserved in manuscript.   Modern editions of his violin music have been prepared by Moffat, Jensen and Schering.   Burney who visited him in Berlin in 1772 had great praise for his adagio playing. (The Present State of Music in Germany and the Netherlands. 1773. v.2. p.128)

C major

1.   Suonata / Del Sig^r: Francesco Benda /   It. 65

score.
23x32.5cm. 10 st.
WM: unclear.
Hand II. Brown.

Listed in Breitkopf supplement, 1776, as no.1 of V Soli del Sig^r. Benda, Racc.XI.

BERTONI, FERDINANDO GIUSEPPE, 1725-1813

Venetian composer, organist and music director. He was a pupil of Padre Martini, was organist and later maestro di cappella at St. Marks, and a prolific composer of church music. He wrote forty-eight operas and some fifteen oratorios, and published at least two sets of keyboard sonatas with accompanying violin. Apart from two trips to London, in 1779/80 and 1781/83, he devoted himself to musical activities in Venice, and was Baldassarre Galuppi's successor at the Conservatorio de' Mendicanti. A Symphony in C Major has been edited by Ettore Bonelli (Padova, 1956).

C major

1.   Sonata a Violino, e Basso / Del / Sig.^r Ferdinando Bertoni /   It. 66

score.
24x32cm. 10 st.
WM: 28.
Hand A. Brown.

Oboe virtuoso active in the royal court of Turin; he was a member of a celebrated family of instrumentalists, oboe and bassoon players, that included two
brothers, Girolamo (1704-78) and Antonio (1714-81) and a nephew, Carlo (1755-
92) son of Antonio. All were composers of chamber music and this fact has led
to some confusion in the attributions assigned to their works. Alessandro and
Girolamo are known to have collaborated in sets of trio sonatas. Chamber music
by Alessandro Besozzi was published in London and Paris, and there are manuscript copies to be found in several European libraries: Paris, London, Padua,
etc.

There are nineteen trio sonatas by Alessandro Besozzi in the Berkeley collection.
Manuscript part books (violin 2 and bass only, not part of the present collection) contain twelve additional trio sonatas and duplicate the following eight:
It. 67, 68, 74, 76, 77, 80, 83 and 86. Another manuscript copy of It. 75 (also
from another source) has a title page dated 1753.

A major

1. Sonata a tre / Del Sig:^{r} Allessandro Besozzi / Basso /

It. 67
v 1 & 2, bass.
22x30.5cm. 8 st.
WM: 14.
Hand A. Brown.

Published as no. 6 of XII Sonates ... par M^{rs}. Bezzossi.
Oeuvre IIe. (Paris, Le Clerc, ca. 1740)

C major

2. Trio / Del Sig:^{r} Allessandro Besozzi / Basso /

It. 68
v 1 & 2, bass.
22.5x30cm. 8 st.
WM: 17.
Hand A. Brown.

Published as no. 4 of XII Sonates ... par M^{rs}. Bezzossi.
Oeuvre IIe. (Paris, Le Clerc, ca. 1740)

C minor

3. Triò / Del Sig.ʳ Allessandro Besozzi / Basso /

It. 69
v 1 & 2, bass.
22.5x30cm. 8 st.
WM: 16.
Hand A. Brown.

D major

4. Trio a due Violini / Col Basso / Del Sig.ʳ Allessandro Besozzi /
   Basso /

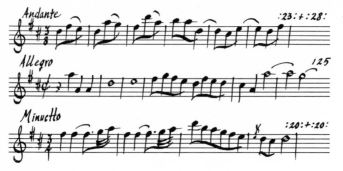

It. 70
v 1 & 2, bass.
22x32cm. 10 st.
WM: 63A.
Hand A. Brown.

5. Triò / Del Sig.ʳ Allessandro Besozzi / Basso /

It. 71
v 1 & 2, bass.
22.5x30cm. 8 st.
WM: 16.
Hand A. Brown.

6. Triò / Del Sig.^r Allessandro Besozzi / Basso /

It. 72
v 1 & 2, bass.
22.5x30cm. 8 st.
WM: 16.
Hand A. Brown.

E flat major

7. Triò / Del Sig:^r Allessandro Besozzi / Basso /

It. 73
v 1 & 2, bass.
22.5x30cm. 8 st.
WM: 16.
Hand A. Brown.

Version for 2 oboes in F major listed in Breitkopf supplement,
1770, as no. 5 of VI Sonate di Alessandro Besozzi a 2 oboi e
basso.

F major

8. Triò / Del Sig:^r Allessandro Besozzi / Basso /

It. 74
v 1 & 2, bass.
22x30cm. 8 st.
WM: 17.
Hand A. Brown.

9. Trio / Del Sig.^r Allessandro Besozzi / Basso /

It. 75
v 1 & 2, bass.
22x29.5cm. 8 st.
WM: 16.
Hand A. Brown.

10. Triò / del Sig:^r Allessandro Besozzi / Basso /

[Violin 2]

It. 76
v 2, bass.
22.5x30cm. 10 st.
WM: 6.
Hand A. Brown.

Published as no. 9 of <u>XII Sonates</u> ... par M^{rs}. Be₂zossi.
<u>Oeuvre IIe</u>. (Paris, Le Clerc, ca. 1740)

G major

11. Trio / Del Sig^r. Allessandro Besozzi / Basso /

It. 77
v 1 & 2, bass.
22x30.5cm. 8 st.
WM: 17.
Hand A. Brown.

Published as no. 1 of <u>XII Sonates</u> ... par M^{rs}. Bezzossi.
<u>Oeuvre IIe</u>. (Paris, Le Clerc, ca. 1740)

12. Trio a due Violini / Con Basso / Del Sig.ʳ Allessandro Besozzi /
    Basso /

It. 78
v 1 & 2, bass.
22x32cm. 10 st.
WM: 63A & 6.
Hand A. Brown.

13. Trio a due Violini / Col Basso / Del Sig:ʳ Allessandro Besozzi /
    Basso /

It. 79
v 1 & 2, bass.
22.5x31.5cm.10 st.
WM: 6.
Hand A. Brown.

14. Trio a due Violini / e Basso / Del Sig.ʳ Allessandro Besozzi /
    Basso /

It. 80
bass.
22.5x30.5cm.10 st.
WM: 6.
Hand A. Brown.

Published as no. 8 of XII Sonates ... par Mʳˢ. Bezzossi.
Oeuvre IIᵉ. (Paris, Le Clerc, ca.1740)

G minor

15. Triô / Del Sig:^r Allessandro Besozzi / Basso /

It. 81
v 1 & 2, bass.
23x30.5cm. 8 st.
WM: 16.
Hand A. Brown.

A major

16. Trio / Del Sig:^r Allessandro Besozzi / Basso /

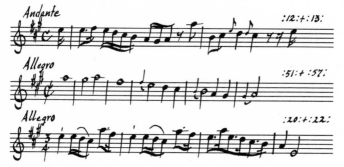

It. 82
v 1 & 2, bass.
22.5x30cm. 8 st.
WM: 16.
Hand A. Brown.

B flat major

17. Triô / Del Sig:^r Allessandro Besozzi / Basso /

It. 83
v 1 & 2, bass.
22.5x30cm. 8 st.
WM: 17.
Hand A. Brown.

Published as no. 11 of XII Sonates ... par M^rs. Bezzossi.
Oeuvre IIe. (Paris, Le Clerc, ca. 1740)

Another copy. Triô / Del Sig: Allessandro Besuzzi / Basso /

It. 84
v 1 & 2, bass.
23x31cm. 10 st.
WM: 21.
Hand LL. Brown.

18. Triô / Del Sig:^r Allessandro Besozzi / Basso /

It. 85
v 1 & 2, bass.
22.5x30cm. 8 st.
WM: 16.
Hand A. Brown.

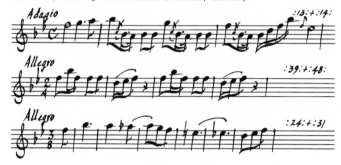

19. Trio a due Violini / Col Basso / Del Sig.^r Allessandro Besozzi /
    Basso /

It. 86
v 1 & 2, bass.
22.5x30.5cm.10 st.
WM: 6.
Hand A. Brown.

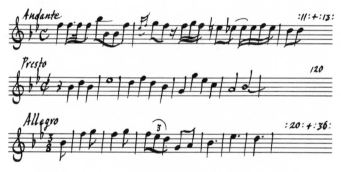

Published as no. 12 of <u>XII Sonates</u> ... <u>par</u> M^{rs}. Bezzossi.
<u>Oeuvre II</u>^e. (Paris, Le Clerc, ca. 1740)

BINI, PASQUALE (PASQUALINO) 1716-1768

Violinist-composer who began studying with Tartini at the age of fifteen under
the patronage of Cardinal Olivieri of Pesaro. Tartini considered him one of his
best pupils. After a period of activity in Rome, first in the service of Cardinal
Olivieri, later under Cardinal Acquaviva, he became, in 1754, director of concerts for Charles-Eugene, Duke of Wurtemberg. All of his surviving works are
in manuscript. Sonatas and concertos are preserved in Berlin, Vienna and
Paris. He is represented in the Berkeley collection by one sonata, five duos
and three concertos.

D major

1. Sonata a Violino è Basso / Del / Sig:ʳ Pasqualino Bini /

It. 87
score.
23x32cm. 10 st.
WM: 12.
Hand A. Brown.

Duets

D major

1. Duetto / Del Sig.ʳ Pasqualino Bini / Violino Primo /

It. 88
v 1 & 2.
23x31.5cm. 10 st.
WM: 3.
Hand A. Brown.

E flat major

2. Duetto / Del Sig.ʳ Pasqualino Bini / Violino Primo /

It. 89
v 1 & 2.
23x32cm. 10 st.
WM: 3.
Hand A. Brown.

G major

3. Duetto / Del Sig.^r Pasqualino Bini / Violino Primo /

It. 90
v 1 & 2.
23x31.5cm. 10 st.
WM: 3.
Hand A. Brown.

A major

4. Duetto / Del Sig.^r Pasqualino Bini / Violino Primo /

It. 91
v 1 & 2.
23.5x32cm. 10 st.
WM: 3.
Hand A. Brown.

B flat major

5. Duetto / Del Sig.^r Pasqualino Bini / Violino Primo /

It. 92
v 1 & 2.
23x32cm. 10 st.
WM: 3.
Hand A. Brown.

Concertos

D major

1. Violino Principale / Concerto / Del / Sig:[r] Pasqualino Bini /

It. 93
vp, v 1 & 2 obl,
vla, bass.
23x31cm. 10 st.
WM: 22.
Hand A. Brown.

Another copy. Concerto grosso / Con Violino Principale, a quattro di / Accompagnamento, è Basso / di Ripieno / Del Sig.[r] / Pasquale Bini Detto Il / Pesarese / [Basso]

It. 94
vp, bass.
25x39cm. 10 st.
(outside leaves
of bass unruled)
WM: 23.
Hand MM. Brown.

F major

2. Violino Principale / Concerto / Del Sig.[r] Pasqualino Bini /

It. 95
vp, v 1 & 2 obl,
vla, vlc obl.
22x30cm. 10 st.
WM: 73.
Hand A. Brown.

Another copy. Violino Principale / Concerto / Del Sig.[r] Domenico dall' Oglio / See It. 356.

G major

3. Violino Principale / Concerto / Del Sig:[r] Pasquale Bini /

It. 96
vp, v 1 & 2 obl,
vla, bass.
22x30cm. 10 st.
WM: 63A.
Hand A. Brown.

Another copy. Concerto grosso / A Violino Solo Con Strumenti /
Basso / Del Sig.[r] / Pasquale Bini detto / il Pesarese /

It. 97
bass.
25x38cm. 10 st.
WM: 23.
Hand MM. Brown.

BOCCHERINI, LUIGI, 1743-1805

1. Sei Duetti / Per due Violini / del Sig:[r] Luigi Boccherini /
Violino Primo /

It. 98
v 1 & 2.
23.5x32cm. 10 st.
WM: 24.
Hand NN. Brown.

G major

Duetto No. 1.

F major

No. 2.

A major

No. 3.

B flat major

No. 4.

E flat major

No. 5.

D major

No. 6.

Listed in Breitkopf supplement, 1771,as no. 1-6 of VI Duetti di
Luigi Bocherini. Opera V. [Intagliati a] Parigi.

BORGHI, LUIGI, b.ca.1745

Pupil of Pugnani. He went to London in 1774, where he was active as a violinist and composer. He participated in the Handel Commemoration in 1784, and
directed a festival of Italian music held at the London Pantheon in 1790. His
instrumental music was published in London, Amsterdam and Berlin. Prints of
his Sei divertimenti, Op.3a (London, ca.1780) and Six solos, Op.1 (London,
ca.1772) are in the University of California Music Library. He is represented
in the manuscript collection by six concertos.

B flat major

1. Borghi / Concerto / No: I / Violoncello Obligato /

It. 99
vp, v 1 & 2, vla,
vlc obl, oboe 1 & 2,
horn 1 & 2.
32x23.5cm. 12 st.
(vp). 22.5x31.5cm.

10 st. (parts)
WM: 25 & 26.
Hand U. Brown.

Listed in Breitkopf supplement, 1776 & 1777, as no.1 of III Conc.
da L. Borghi ... Op. II. [Intagliati a] Amst.

E flat major

2. Borghi / Concerto II / Violoncello Obligato /

It. 100
vp, v 1 & 2, vla,
vlc obl, bass,
oboe 1 & 2, horn
1 & 2.
31.5x22.5cm. 12 st.
(vp). 22.5x31.5cm.
10 st. (parts)
WM: 20.
Hand U. Brown.

Listed in Breitkopf supplement, 1776 & 1777, as no.2 of III Conc.
da L. Borghi ... Op. II. [Intagliati a] Amst.

D major

3. Borghi / Concerto III / Violoncello Obligato /

It. 101
vp, v 1 & 2, vla,
vlc obl, bass,
flute 1 & 2, horn
1 & 2.
31x22.5cm. 12 st.
(vp). 22.5x31cm.
10 st. (parts)
WM: 20.
Hand U. Brown.

Listed in Breitkopf supplement, 1776 & 1777, as no.3 of III Conc.
da L. Borghi ... Op. II. [Intagliati a] Amst.

C major

4.   Borghi / Violoncello Obligato / IV /

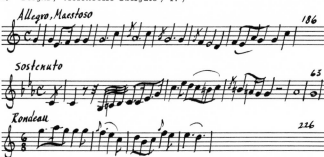

It. 102
vp, v 1 & 2, vla,
vlc obl, bass,
oboe 1 & 2, horn
1 & 2.
32x22cm. 12 st.
(vp). 22.5x31cm.
10 st. (parts)
WM: 20.
Hand U. Brown.

Listed in Breitkopf supplement, 1776 & 1777, as no. 4 of III Conc.
da L. Borghi ... Op. III. [Intagliati a] Amst.

G minor

5.   Borghi / Violoncello Obligato / Concerto V. /

It. 103
vp, v 1 & 2, vla,
vlc obl, bass,
oboe 1 & 2, horn
1 & 2.
31.5x22.5cm. 12 st.
(vp). 22.5x31.5cm.
10 st. (parts)
WM: 20.
Hand U. Brown.

Listed in Breitkopf supplement, 1776 & 1777, as no. 5 of III Conc.
da L. Borghi ... Op. III. [Intagliati a] Amst.

E major

6.   Borghi / Concerto N:° VI /Violoncello /

It. 104
vp, v 1 & 2, vla,
vlc, oboe 1 & 2,
horn 1 & 2.
31.5x23.5cm. 12 st.
(vp). 22.5x32cm.
10 st. (parts)
WM: 25 & 20.
Hand U. Brown.

Listed in Breitkopf supplement, 1776 & 1777, as no. 6 of III Conc.
da L. Borghi ... Op. III. [Intagliati a] Amst.

Very little is known about this musician.   Torrefranca identifies his style with
that of the school of Milan of about 1745 (Le Sinfonie dell'Imbrattacarte, Turin,
1915, p. 121).   Twenty-eight works by this composer are in the Fonds Blancheton of the Bibliothèque du Conservatoire, Paris.   Trio sonatas by Brioschi, in company with J. B. Sammartini and others, were published in a collection by Walsh,
London, 1746.   According to La Laurencie, there is a collection of eighteen Sinfonie in the Bibliothek at Darmstadt.   Three Sinfonie a 3, and one Sinfonie a 4
are in the Berkeley collection.

E flat major

1.   Violino Primo /

It. 105
v 1 & 2, bass.
23.5x30.5cm. 10 st.
WM: 27.
Hand B. Black.

Another copy.   Sinfonia a 3 / Del Sig[r]: Antonio Brioshi /
Violino Pmo: /

It. 106
v 1.
23.5x30cm. 10 st.
WM: 27.
Hand G. Black.
(title in Hand B)

B flat major

2.   Sinfonia a 3 / Del Sig:[r] Antonio Brioschi / Violino Pmo: /

It. 107
v 1 & 2, bass.
23.5x31cm. 10 st.
WM: 27.
Hand B. Black.

3.   Sinfonia a 3 / Del Sig:^r Antonio Brioschi / Violino Pmo: /

It. 108
v 1 & 2, bass.
24x31cm. 10 st.
WM: 27.
Hand B. Black.

Listed by La Laurencie in Inventaire ... du fonds Blancheton,
p. 44, as Trio Del Signor Antonio Brioschi a Tre Stromenti.

Quartets

E flat major

1.   Sinfonia a 4 / Del Sig:^r Antonio Brioschi / Violino Pmo: /

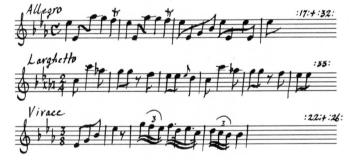

It. 109
v 1 & 2, vla, bass.
22.5x31cm. 10 st.
WM: 27.
Hand B. Black.

CAMERLOHER, PLACIDUS VON, 1718-1782

Bavarian composer active for most of his career in Freising. He composed much
instrumental music preserved in manuscripts and early prints in several European libraries: twenty-six symphonies, five trios and fifteen sonatas in Darmstadt, twenty-nine symphonies in Munich, twelve sinfonie da camera, Op. III,
and six sinfonie à 4, Op. IV, in the Bibliothèque du Conservatoire, Paris, and
twelve sinfonie and twelve concertini in the Blancheton collection of that library.
An orchestral quartet in F major and three Freisinger Sinfonien have recently
been edited in modern edition by Adolf Hoffmann (Corona, Werkreihe für Kammer-
orchester, Wölfenbüttel, 1957-58)

B flat major

1.   Trio / A Due Violini, e Violoncello / Del Sig.^{r} Camerloker /

It. 110
v 1 & 2, vlc.
23x32cm. 10 st.
WM: 68.
Hand A. Brown.

Listed in Breitkopf supplement, 1762, as no.1 of VI Sonate a due Violini e Basso, del Sign. Cammerlocher. Racc.IV.

CAMPIONI, CARLO ANTONIO, 1720-1793

Violinist and composer of instrumental and church music. Maestro di cappella in Florence, 1764-80. Burney met him in Florence in 1770 and observed, "He has the greatest collection of old music, particularly Madrigals, of the 16th and 17th centuries, Padre Martini's excepted, that I ever saw." (Burney, Musical Tour ... I, p.187) Editions of his instrumental music appeared in London, Paris and Amsterdam.

Of the 29 Campioni trios in the present collection, 25 appear in the London prints of Op.I-V published by Walsh.

C major

1.   Sonata a tre / Del Sig.^{r} Carlo Antonio Campioni / Basso /

It. 111
v 1 & 2, bass.
22x30.5cm. 10 st.
WM: 28.
Hand A. Black.

Published as op.2 no.6 (London, Walsh, 1758)

D major

2.   Sonata a trè / Del Sig.^r Carlo Antonio Campioni / Basso /

It. 112
v 1 & 2, bass.
22x30cm. 10 st.
WM: 28.
Hand A. Brown.

Published as op. 2 no. 3 (London, Walsh, 1758)

3.   Sonata a trè / Del Sig:^r Carlo Antonio Campioni / Basso /

It. 113
v 1 & 2, bass.
22x31cm. 10 st.
WM: 28.
Hand A. Black.

Published as op. 3 no. 5 (London, Walsh, 1759)

E major

4.   Sonata a trè / Del Sig:^r Carlo Antonio Campioni / Basso /

It. 114
v 1 & 2, bass.
22x31.5cm. 10 st.
WM: 28.
Hand A. Black.

Published as op. 3 no. 2 (London, Walsh, 1759)

F major

5.   Sonata a tre / Del Sig.^r Carlo Antonio Campioni / Basso /

It. 115
v 1 & 2, bass.
21.5x30cm. 10 st.
WM: 28.
Hand A. Black.

Published as op. 2 no. 4 (London, Walsh, 1758)

G minor

6.   Sonata a tre / Del Sig:^r Carlo Antonio Campioni / Basso /

It. 116
v 1 & 2, bass.
22x30.5cm. 10 st.
WM: 28 & 29.
Hand A. Black.

Published as op. 1 no. 2 (London, Walsh, ca. 1760)

A major

7.   Sonata a tre / Del Sig:^r Carlo Antonio Campioni / Basso /

It. 117
v 1 & 2, bass.
22x30.5cm. 10 st.
WM: 28 & 6.
Hand A. Black.

Published as op. 1 no. 6 (London, Walsh, ca. 1760)

<u>C major</u>

8. Triò / Del Sig.^r Antonio Campioni / Basso /

It. 118
v 1 & 2, bass.
22.5x31cm. 10 st.
WM: 6.
Hand A. Black.

Published as op.1 no.5 (London, Walsh, ca.1760)

9. Trio / Del Sig:^r Carlo Antonio Campioni / Basso /

It. 119
v 1 & 2, bass.
23x32cm. 10 st.
WM: 28 & 29.
Hand A. Brown.

With a different minuet, published as op.5 no.4 (London, Walsh,
ca.1760)

10. Basso. Trio del Sig:^r Carlo Antonio Campioni /

It. 120
v 1 & 2, bass.
23x32cm. 10 st.
WM: 29.
Hand A. Brown.

Caption title.
Published as op.4 no.3 (London, Walsh, ca.1765)

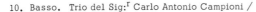

11. Triö / del Sig.^r Antonio Campioni / Basso /

It. 121
v 1 & 2, bass.
22.5x31cm. 10 st.
WM: 6.
Hand A. Brown.

Published as op. 3 no. 3 (London, Walsh, 1759)

D major

12. Trio / Del Sig:^r Carlo Antonio Campioni / Basso /

It. 122
v 1 & 2, bass.
23x32.5cm. 10 st.
WM: 28 & 29.
Hand A. Brown.

Adagio and minuetto published in op. 5 no. 2 (London, Walsh, ca. 1760)   Allegro published as Allegretto in op. 5 no. 5 (London, Walsh, ca. 1760)

13. Violino primo. Trio Del Sig:^r Carlo Antonio Campioni /

It. 123
v 1 & 2, bass.
23x32cm. 10 st.
WM: 28.
Hand A. Brown.

Caption title.
Published as op. 4 no. 1 (London, Walsh, ca. 1765)

14. Triỏ / Del Sig:^{r} C:^{o} A:^{o} Campionj / Basso /

It. 124
v 1 & 2, bass.
22.5x30cm. 10 st.
WM: unclear.
Hand A. Brown.

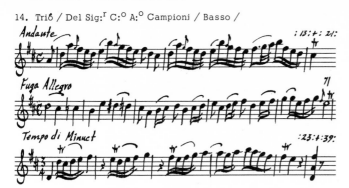

Published as op. 2 no. 1 (London, Walsh, 1758)

E flat major

15. Trio / Del Sig:^{r} Carlo Antonio Campioni / Basso /

It. 125
v 1 & 2, bass.
23x32cm. 10 st.
WM: 29.
Hand A. Brown.

E major

16. Trio / Del Sig:^{r} Carlo Antonio Campioni / Basso /

It. 126
v 1 & 2, bass.
23x32cm. 10 st.
WM: 29.
Hand A. Brown.

F major

17. Trio / Del Sig:^r Carlo Antonio Campioni / Basso /

It. 127
v 1 & 2, bass.
23x32cm. 10 st.
WM: 28 & 29.
Hand A. Brown.

Published as op. 5 no. 3 (London, Walsh, ca. 1760)

18. Trio / Del Sig:^r Antonio Campioni / Basso /

It. 128
v 1 & 2, bass.
22.5x31cm. 10 st.
WM: 6.
Hand A. Brown.

Published as op. 1 no. 1 (London, Walsh, ca. 1760)

G major

19. Basso.   Trio del Sig.^r Carlo Antonio Campioni /

It. 129
v 1 & 2, bass.
23x32.5cm. 10 st.
WM: 29.
Hand A. Brown.

Caption title.
Published as op. 3 no. 6 (London, Walsh, 1759)

20. Trio / del Sig:ʳ C:º A:º Campioni / Basso /

It. 130
v 1& 2, bass.
22x30.5cm. 8 st.
WM: 53.
Hand A. Brown.

Published as op. 2 no. 2 (London, Walsh, 1758)

21. Trio / del Sig:ʳ Carlo Antonio Campioni / Basso /

It. 131
v 1& 2, bass.
23x32cm. 10 st.
WM: 29.
Hand A. Brown.

Published as op. 5 no. 1 (London, Walsh, ca. 1760)

22. Trio / Del Sig:ʳ Antonio Campioni / Basso /

It. 132
v 1& 2, bass.
22.5x31.5cm. 10 st.
WM: 6.
Hand A. Brown.

Published as op. 3 no. 6 (London, Walsh, 1759)

23. Trio / Del Sig.^{r} Carlo Antonio Campioni / Basso /

It. 133
v 1 & 2, bass.
22.5x30cm. 10 st.
WM: 6.
Hand A. Brown.

24. Trio / Del Sig:^{r} Carlo Antonio Campioni / Basso /

It. 134
v 1 & 2, bass.
22.5x30.5cm. 10 st.
WM: 6.
Hand A. Brown.

Published as op. 3 no. 1 (London, Walsh, 1759)

G minor

25. Violino primo. Trio Del Sig:^{r} Carlo Antonio Campioni /

It. 135
v 1 & 2, bass.
23x32cm. 10 st.
WM: 29.
Hand A. Brown.

Caption title.
Published as op. 4 no. 2 (London, Walsh, ca. 1765)

A major

26. Trio / Del Sig.^r Carlo Antonio Campioni / Basso /

It. 136
v 1 & 2, bass.
22.5x30cm. 10 st.
WM: 53.
Hand A. Brown.

27. Triô Del Sig:^r Campioni / Basso /

It. 137
v 1 & 2, bass.
22x30cm. 8 st.
WM: unclear.
Hand A. Brown.

Caption title.
Published as op. 2 no. 5 (London, Walsh, 1758)

B flat major

28. Trio / Del Sig^r Campioni / Basso /

It. 138
v 1 & 2, bass.
23.5x31.5cm. 10 st.
WM: 58.
Hand BB. Brown.

Incipit on t. p.
Published as op. 1 no. 3 (London, Walsh, ca. 1760)

B minor

29. Trio / Del Sig.^r Carlo Antonio Campioni / Basso /

It. 139
v 1 & 2, bass.
22.5x31cm. 10 st.
WM: 6.
Hand A.   Brown.

Published as op. 3 no. 4 (London, Walsh, 1759)

CAPUZZI, GIUSEPPE ANTONIO, 1755-1818

Violinist-composer active in Venice and Bergamo. He was first violinist in the Teatro S. Samuele in Venice from 1780 to 1785, then director of the orchestra at S. Benedetto. After a visit to London 1796, where he was engaged in writing and producing ballets, he returned to Italy in 1805 to become solo violinist for for the church of S. Maria Maggiore in Bergamo. Grove cites him as a pupil of Tartini. The Dizionario Ricordi, on the other hand, suggests that Tartini's influence was transmitted indirectly through studies with A. Nazari and Bertoni. Besides eleven ballets and an opera, Capuzzi composed sinfonie concertanti, divertimenti, quartets and quintets. Six quartets and three concertos are found in the Berkeley collection. No other examples of his work in concerto form have been cited in bibliographies.

E flat major

1. No. VI. / Quartetti / Per due Violini, Viola, e Basso / Composti dal Sig:^r / Antonio Capucci / Opera II / Violino Primo /

It. 140
v 1 (incomplete)
23x31.5cm. 10 st.
WM: unclear.
Hand PP. Black.

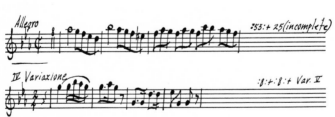

Initials: F. Z. in upper right corner.

Concertos

D major

1. In D:ʳᵉ 3º / Concerto / per Violino. Con Stromti. / Del Sig:ʳ
    Antonio Capucci / Violino Principale /

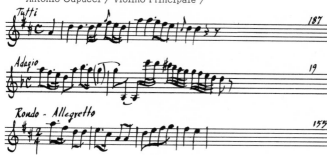

It. 141
vp, v 1 & 2 conc,
vla, vlc, oboe 1
& 2, horn 1 & 2.
23x31.5cm. 10 st.
WM: 47 & 30.
Hand J. Brown.

B flat major

2. In B:fa / Concerto / Per Violino. Con Stromti. / Del Sig:ʳ
    Antonio Capucci / Violino Principale /

It. 142
vp, v 1 & 2 conc,
vla, vlc, oboe 1
& 2, horn 1 & 2.
23x32cm. 10 st.
WM: 47 & 88.
Hand J. Brown.

3. In B:fa. Rec:ᵛᵒ / Concerto / Per Violino. Con Stromti. / Del
    Sig:ʳ Antonio Capucci / Violino Principale /

It. 143
vp, v 1 & 2 conc,
vla, vlc conc,
oboe 1 & 2, horn 1
& 2.
23x31cm. 10 st.
WM: 47, 30 &
unclear.
Hand J. Brown.

Nothing is known about this musician beyond the fact that he was active in Naples around 1780. The <u>British Union-Catalogue of Early Music</u> cites collections of duos and trio sonatas published in Paris, ca. 1780 and 1778, and a collection of quintets issued in Lyon, ca. 1790.

A major

1. Duetto del Sig.^r D. Prospero Caucelli / Violino Primo /

It. 144
v 1 & 2.
23x31.5cm. 10 st.
WM: 3.
Hand A. Brown.

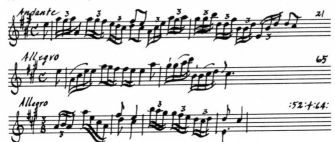

Caption title.

CONTI, PIETRO, fl. 1750

Nothing is known of the biography of this musician. Gerber's <u>Lexikon</u> (1790) makes reference to a violin concerto in manuscript. Eitner cites the presence of a violin piece by this composer in Michael Corette's <u>L'art de se Perfectionner dans le Violon,</u> and manuscripts of duos in the library of the conservatory in Milan, and of a symphony in Schwerin. The Breitkopf & Härtel <u>Catalogo delle Sinfonie</u> ... IV, cites six <u>sinfonie</u>, also in manuscript.

F major

1. Violino Principale / Concerto / Del Sig.^r Pietro Conti /

It. 145
vp, v 1 & 2 obl,
vla obl, [vlc]
23x32cm. 10 st.
WM: 31.
Hand A. Brown.

1. [Opera V. Sonate a Violino e Violone o Cimbalo]   It. 146
                                                                score.
                                                                21.5x31cm. 10 st.
    Without title.   WM: 26.
    Published Rome, Gasparo Pietro Santa, 1700.   Hand RR. Brown.

    see also Geminiani, Francesco. It. 209, 210.

2. 1728 / Baletti del Corelli /

    see Albinoni, Tomaso. It. 63.

DALL'OGLIO, DOMENICO

    see Oglio, Domenico dall'

DE GIOVANNINI, FILIPPO

    see Giovannini, Filippo de

DEMACHI, GIUSEPPE, fl. 1740-1790

    Violinist and composer, born in Alessandria (Piedmont). He was a member of
    the court orchestra at Turin about 1740, and active in Geneva in 1771. Instru-
    mental music by Demachi was published in London, Paris and Lyon, and in-
    cludes concertos, orchestral quartets, trios and sinfonie concertanti. A sona-
    ta from his Op.1 was published in Cartier's L'Art du Violon.

                                    B flat major

1. I. / Sei / Duetto a Due Violini / Del Sig.ʳ Giuseppe Demachi /   It. 147
    Violino Primo /   v 1 & 2.
                                                                     23x31.5cm. 10 st.
                                                                     WM: 3.
                                                                     Hand A. Brown.

Gerber's <u>Lexicon</u> (1790) has entries for two violinists from Bergamo, one a Nazario Deeh, who appeared as a director of the public concerts in Zurich in 1749, another named Nassovius Dehec, who was first violinist in the church of St. Maria Maggiore in Bergamo and had six trios engraved in Nuremberg in about 1760. This information has been perpetuated in the subsequent dictionaries of Choron & Fayolle, Fetis and Eitner. Probably both entries refer to the same man. The <u>British Union-Catalogue of Early Music</u> lists concertos and sonatas by Nazario Dehec as published in 1765.

C major

1. Trio / A Due Violini, e Basso / Del Sig.^r Nazario Dhè / Basso /

It. 148
v 1 & 2, bass.
22.5x31.5cm. 10 st.
WM: 4.
Hand A. Brown.

DOTHEL (DÒTHEL, DÖTHEL) NICOLÒ, fl. 1750

Sonatas, divertimentos and duets for violins or German flute by this composer were published in London, 1755-64; six trio sonatas in manuscript are preserved in the Cappella Antoniana in Padua and are listed in Tebaldini's catalogue of that archive. <u>Eitner</u> refers to Dothel as a flutist. He is otherwise unknown.

D major

1. Sonata da Camera / à 3è / Del Sig.^r Dothel /

It. 149
v 1 & 2 [bass]
22.5x31.5cm. 10 st.
WM: 3 & 4.
Hand A. Brown.

<u>Another copy</u>. Trio à due Violini / Col Basso / Del Sig^r Nicolò
Dothel / Basso /

It. 150
v 1 & 2, bass.
21.5x31cm. 10 st.
WM: 32.
Hand A. Brown.

E minor

2.   Sonata da Camera / a 3ª / Del Sig.ʳ Dothel /

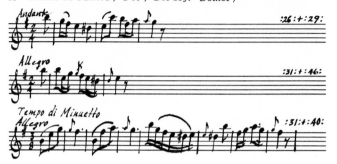

It. 151
v 1 & 2 [bass]
22.5x31.5cm. 10 st.
WM: 3 & 4.
Hand A. Brown.

Another copy. Trio à due Violini / Col Basso / Del Sig:ʳ
Nicolò Dothel / Basso /

It. 152
v 1 & 2, bass.
21.5x30.5cm. 10 st.
WM: 73.
Hand A. Brown.

G major

3.   Sonata da Camera / a 3ᵉ / Del Sig.ʳ Dothel /

It. 153
v 1 & 2 [bass]
22.5x32cm. 10 st.
WM: 4.
Hand A. Brown.

Another copy. Trio / Del Sig:ʳ Nicolò Dothel / Basso /

It. 154
v 1 & 2, bass.
22.5x29.5cm. 10 st.
WM: 53.
Hand A. Brown.

4. Sonata da Camera / a 3^è / Del Sig.^r Dothel /

It. 155
v 1 & 2 [bass]
22.5x32cm. 10 st.
WM: 4.
Hand A. Brown.

<u>Another copy</u>. Trio à due Violini / Col Basso / Del Sig.^r
Nicolò Dothel / Basso /

It. 156
v 1 & 2, bass.
21.5x30.5cm. 10 st.
WM: 73.
Hand A. Brown.

5. Sonata da Camera / a 3^è / Del Sig.^r Dothel /

It. 157
v 1 & 2 [bass]
22.5x32cm. 10 st.
WM: 4.
Hand A. Brown.

<u>Another copy</u>. Trio à due Violini / Col Basso / Del Sig:^r
Nicolò Dothel / Basso /

It. 158
v 1 & 2, bass.
22x30cm. 10 st.
WM: 32.
Hand A. Brown.

A minor

6. Sonata da Camera / a 3ᵉ / Del Sig.ʳ Dothel / Basso /

It. 159
v 1 & 2, bass.
22.5x32cm. 10 st.
WM: 4.
Hand A. Brown.

Another copy. Trio à due Violini / Col Basso / Del Sigʳ
Nicolò Dothel / Basso /

It. 160
v 1 & 2, bass.
22x30.5cm. 10 st.
WM: 32.
Hand A. Brown.

DUSCHMALUI, GIUSEPPE FRANCESE

see Touchemoulin, Joseph

DUTILLIEU, PIERRE, 1754-1797

A French musician, born in Lyon, active in Naples as a composer of ballet and opera until 1791, after which he became Cimarosa's successor at the court in Vienna. Selections from his Gli Accidenti della Villa were printed in J. André's Neue Theater-Gesaenge (1797). According to Larousse de la Musique, he wrote a violin concerto and six duos for two violins.

F major

1. Concerto à / Violino Solo è Strumenti / Del Sig:ᵒʳ / Dutillieu /

It. 161
vp, v 1 & 2 obl,
vla obl, bass obl,
oboe 1 & 2 obl,
horn 1 & 2.
22x30.5cm. 10 st.
WM: 33.
Hand SS. Brown.

Born at Piacenza, he was one of the noted violinists of his time. He was a pupil of Tartini and was active successively at Cremona, Vienna, Württemberg
(where he was a member of the orchestra at the same time as Nardini) and Paris. He
died in 1780 in the course of a journey to London. He was a brother of Carlo
Ferrari, famous as a cellist and composer. Domenico's published works include
six sets of violin sonatas, trio sonatas and Italian and French songs.

C major

1. Sonata a Violino, e Basso / Del Sig:[r] / Domenico Ferrari /

It. 162
score.
23.5x32cm. 10 st.
WM: 78.
Hand B. Black.

D major

2. Sonata a Violino, e Basso / Del Sig:[r] / Domenico Ferrari /

It. 163
score.
23x32cm. 10 st.
WM: 78.
Hand B. Black.

Possibly by Tartini. Listed by Brainard as D.21.

Another copy. Sonata a Violino e Basso / Del Sig[r] Domenico
Ferrari.

It. 164
score.
23x22.5cm. 10 st.
WM: 5.
Hand B. Black.

B flat major

1. Violino / Primo Trio / del Sig[r] Domenico Ferrari /

It. 165
v l.
23x31cm. 10 st.
WM: unclear.
Hand BB. Brown.

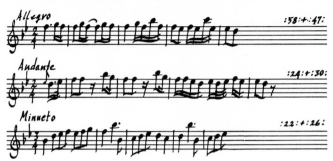

FRACASSINI, ALOISIO LODOVICO, 1733-1798

An eminent violinist, composer and teacher, and a pupil of Tartini. On Tartini's recommendation, Fracassini was appointed in 1757 as first violinist at the combined court chapel of Würzburg and Bamberg. When the chapel was divided in 1779, Fracassini remained at Bamberg until his death in 1798. He was also active as an opera director, and has been credited with playing an important role in transmitting the influence of the Tartini school of violin performance into southern Germany (see MGG, vol. 4, article by Hanns Dennerlein). Examples of his work, including an oratorio, are in the archives at Bamberg. The Berkeley collection has seven of his violin sonatas.

D major

1. Sonata / A Violino e Basso / Del Sig:[r] Luigi Fracassini /

It. 166
score.
22.5x32cm. 10 st.
WM: 4.
Hand H. Brown.

2.   Sonata a Violino, e Basso / Del Sig^r Luigi Fracassini /   It. 167

score.
23x32cm. 10 st.
WM: 34.
Hand B. Black.

Another copy. Suonata / A Violino e Basso / Del Sig^r: Luigi   It. 168
Fracassini /

score.
23x32cm. 12 st.
WM: 40.
Hand II. Brown.

E flat major

3.   Suonata / A / Violino e Basso / Del Sig^r: Luigi Fracasini /   It. 169

score.
23x32cm. 10 st.
WM: 89.
Hand II. Brown.

E major

4.   Suonata a Violino e Basso / Del Sig^r: Luigi Fracasini /   It. 170

score.
22.5x31cm. 10 st.
WM: 90.
Hand II. Brown.

Another copy. Sonata a Violino e Basso / Del Sig:[r] Luigi   It. 171
Fracassini /   score.
                                                                23x32cm. 10 st.
                                                                WM: 34.
                                                                Hand B. Black.

5.   Suonata / A Violino e Basso / Del Sig[r]: Luigi Fracasini /   It. 172
                                                                score.

                                                                23x32.5cm. 10 st.
                                                                WM: 3.
                                                                Hand II. Brown.

6.   Suonata / A / Violino e Basso / Del Sig[r]: Luigi Fracasini /   It. 173
                                                                score.

                                                                23x32.5cm. 10 st.
                                                                WM: 89.
                                                                Hand II. Brown.

Another copy. Sonata / a Violino e Basso / Del Sig:[r] / Luigi   It. 174
Fracassini /   score.
                                                                23.5x32.5cm. 10 st.
                                                                WM: 91.
                                                                Hand B. Black.

B flat major

7.   Suonata / A Violino e Basso / Del Sig.^r: Luigi Fracasini /   It. 175
score.
23x32cm. 10 st.
WM: 35.
Hand II. Brown.

FRITZ, KASPAR, 1716-1782

Violinist, composer and teacher, born in Geneva where he spent the greater part
of his life. He was a pupil of Giovanni Battista Somis in Turin. Instrumental
music by Fritz, including solo violin sonatas, sonate à quattro, and symphonies,
were published in London, Paris and Vienna. The Berkeley collection contains
manuscripts of six trio sonatas.

1.   N.° VI / Sonate a Tre / Del Sig.^r Fritz / Violino Primo /   It. 176
v 1 & 2, bass.
23.5x32.5cm. 10 st.
WM: 36.
D major   Hand A. Brown.

I.

B flat major

II.

E flat major

III.

A major

IV.

D major

D minor

GALEOTTI (GALLEOTTI)

Two musicians named Galeotti, Salvatore and Stefano, lived in London during the latter half of the 18th century and published instrumental music there. No references have been found to an Antonio, whose name appears on six trio sonatas in the Berkeley collection. Five of the remaining twelve trio sonatas were published by Welcker in 1762 as works of Salvatore Galleotti.

<u>C major</u>

1. Violino Primo / Sonata à Trê / Del Sig.^r Antonio Galeotti /

It. 177
v 1 & 2, bass.
23x31.5cm. 10 st.
WM: 3 & 37.
Hand A². Black.

<u>Another copy</u>. Trið / del Sig^r: Galleotti / Basso /

It. 178
v 1 & 2, bass.
22.5x32cm. 10 st.
WM: 32.
Hand II. Brown.

<u>E flat major</u>

2. Violino Primo / Sonata à Trê / Del Sig.^r Antonio Galeotti /

It. 179
v 1 & 2, bass.
22x31cm. 10 st.
WM: 98 & 37.
Hand A². Black.

<u>Another copy</u>. Trið / Del Signor Galleotti / Basso /

It. 180
v 1 & 2, bass.
23x32cm. 10 st.
WM: 32 & 38.
Hand II. Brown.

F major

3.   Violino Primo / Sonata à Trê / Del Sig.[r] Antonio Galeotti /

It. 181
v 1 & 2, bass.
22.5x31.5cm. 10 st.
WM: 35.
Hand A[2]. Black.

Another copy. Triò / del Sig:[r] Galleotti / Basso /

It. 182
v 1 & 2, bass.
22.5x31cm. 10 st.
WM: 32.
Hand II. Brown.

G major

4.   Violino P:[mo] / Sonata à Tre / Del Sig.[r] Antonio Galeotti /

It. 183
v 1 & 2, bass.
22.5x31.5cm. 10 st.
WM: 35.
Hand A[2]. Brown.

Another copy. Triò / Del Sig:[r] Galleotti / Basso /

It. 184
v 1 & 2, bass.
22.5x32cm. 10 st.
WM: unclear.
Hand H[2]. Brown.

A major

5.   Violino Primo / Sonata a Tre / Del Sig.[r] Antonio Galeotti /

It. 185
v 1 & 2, bass.
22.5x31.5cm. 10 st.
WM: 35.
Hand A[2]. Brown.

Another copy. Triò / Del Sig[r]. Galleotti / Basso /

It. 186
v 1 & 2, bass.
22.5x31.5cm. 10 st.
WM: 32.
Hand II. Brown.

B flat major

6.   Violino Primo / Sonata à Tre / Del Sig.[r] Antonio Galeotti /

It. 187
v 1 & 2, bass.
22.5x31.5cm. 10 st.
WM: 37.
Hand A[2]. Black.

Another copy. Triò / del Sig.[r] Galleotti / Basso /

It. 188
v 1 & 2, bass.
23x31.5cm. 10 st.
WM: 32.
Hand II. Brown.

D major

7. Trið / Del Sig:ʳ Galleotti / Basso /

It. 189
v 1 & 2, bass.
22.5x31.5cm. 10 st.
WM: 39.
Hand H². Brown.
(title in Hand B)

Published London, Welcker, 1762, with composer's name
given as Salvatore Galleotti.

E major

8. Trið / Del Sig:ʳ Galleotti / Basso /

It. 190
v 1& 2, bass.
23x32cm. 10 st.
WM: 98.
Hand H². Brown.
(title in Hand B)

Published London, Welcker, 1762, with composer's name
given as Salvatore Galleotti.

F major

9. Trið / Del Sig:ʳ Galleotti / Basso /

It. 191
v 1& 2, bass.
22.5x33cm. 10 st.
WM: 39.
Hand H². Brown.
(title in Hand B)

G major

10. Trio / Del Sig:ʳ Galleotti / Basso /

It. 192
v 1 & 2, bass.
22.5x32cm. 10 st.
WM: 39.
Hand H². Brown.
(title in Hand B)

Published London, Welcker, 1762, with composer's name
given as Salvatore Galleotti.

A major

11. Trio / Del Sig:ʳ Galleotti / Basso /

It. 193
v 1 & 2, bass.
23x32.5cm. 10 st.
WM: 39.
Hand H². Brown.
(title in Hand B)

Published London, Welcker, 1762, with composer's name
given as Salvatore Galleotti.

B flat major

12. Trio / Del Sig:ʳ Galleotti / Basso /

It. 194
v 1 & 2, bass.
22.5x31.5cm. 10 st.
WM: 39.
Hand H². Brown.
(title in Hand B)

Published London, Welcker, 1762, with composer's name
given as Salvatore Galleotti.

Van der Straeten suggests that this musician was born in Venice, and cites a copy of six trio sonatas published in Venice, now in the library of the Milan conservatory. Six sonatas for two flutes and bass were printed for Oswald, London, about 1755, and the Breitkopf & Härtel Catalogo delle Sinfonie ... Supplemento I (1766) lists a sinfonia à 4. Seven trio sonatas by Gallo are found in the Berkeley collection.

D major

1. Sonata a Trè / Del Sig.ʳ Gallo / Basso /

It. 195
v 1 & 2, bass.
22.5x30.5cm. 10 st.
WM: 63A.
Hand A. Brown.

E major

2. Sonata a due Violini, e / Basso del / Sig:ʳ Domenico Gallo / Violino Primo /

It. 196
v 1 & 2, bass.
23x31.5cm. 10 st.
WM: 25.
Hand G. Black.

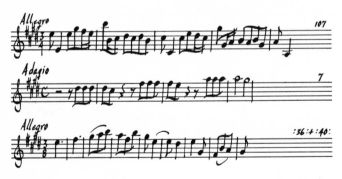

G minor

3. Sonata a Trè / Del Sig:^r Gallo / Basso /

It. 197
v 1 & 2, bass.
22x30.5cm. 8 st.
WM: 50.
Hand A. Brown.

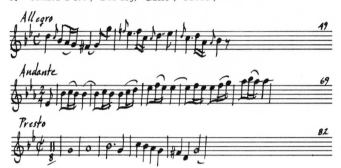

A major

4. Sonata a Trè / Del Sig.^r Gallo / Basso /

It. 198
v 1 & 2, bass.
22.5x30.5cm. 10 st.
WM: 63A.
Hand A. Brown.

B flat major

5. Sonata a Trè / Del Sig.^r Gallo / Basso /

It. 199
v 1 & 2, bass.
22x31cm. 10 st.
WM: 63A.
Hand A. Brown.

B minor

6.   Sonata a Trè / Del / Sig.ʳ Gallo /Basso /

It. 200
v 1 & 2, bass.
22.5x30.5cm. 10 st.
WM: 63A.
Hand A. Brown.

A major

7.   Basso / Trio / Del Sig:ʳ Gallo /

It. 201
v 1 & 2, bass.
21x30cm. 10 st.
WM: 17.
Hand A. Brown.

GASPARINI, PIETRO

No musician of this name is mentioned in any of the available reference works. There is a Francesco Gasparini, 1668-1737, who was active as a composer of Italian operas in London during the early years of the 18th century. Six trio sonatas were published in London under his name, in two editions, ca. 1760 and ca. 1765. Van der Straeten has expressed doubt that these works could have been written by Francesco. It is possible that Pietro Gasparini, represented in the Berkeley collection by seven trio sonatas, was the composer to whom the London trios should be attributed.

G major

1. Sonatina da Camera / Del Sig.^r Gasparini / Basso /

It. 202
v 1 & 2, bass.
23.5x32cm. 10 st.
WM: 16 & 68.
Hand A. Brown.

G minor

2. Sonatina da Camera / Del Sig.^r Gasparini / Basso /

It. 203
v 1 & 2, bass.
22.5x32cm. 10 st.
WM: 68.
Hand A. Brown.

C minor

3. Trio / Del Sig:^r Pietro Gasparini / Violino Primo /

It. 204
v 1 & 2, bass.
23x30cm. 8 st.
WM: 16.
Hand A. Brown.

Listed in Breitkopf supplement, 1776, as no. 5 of VI Trii del Sig^r.
Gasparini a 2 Viol. e Basso.

E flat major

4. Trio / Del Sig.ʳ Pietro Gasparini / Violino Primo /

It. 205
v 1 & 2, bass.
22x30cm. 8 st.
WM: 16.
Hand A. Brown.

F major

5. Trio / Del Sig.ʳ Pietro Gasparini / Violino Primo /

It. 206
v 1 & 2, bass.
22.5x30.5cm. 8 st.
WM: 16.
Hand A. Brown.

A major

6. Trio / Del Sig.ʳ Pietro Gasparini / Basso /

It. 207
v 1 & 2, bass.
23x32cm. 10 st.
WM: 29 & 16.
Hand A. Brown.

7. Trio / Del Sig:^r Pietro Gasparini / Violino Primo /

It. 208
v 1&2, bass.
22.5x30cm. 8 st.
WM: 16 & 28.
Hand A. Brown.

GEMINIANI, FRANCESCO, 1679 or 80-1762

A pupil of Corelli, he was one of the greatest violin composer-teachers of his time. He was born in Lucca, and was concert master of the orchestra in Naples until he came to London in 1714 where he. spent the greater part of his career. He arranged Corelli's violin sonatas, Op.5 as concerti grossi, published by Walsh and Hare in 1726-28 as Concerti Grossi . . . Composti delli Sei Soli della prima parte dell' Opera Quinta D'Arcangelo Corelli (sonatas 1-6); Seconda Parte (sonatas 7-12). These are the works which appear in manuscript parts in the Berkeley collection. Geminiani's treatise, The Art of Playing on the Violin, has been edited in facsimile by David Boyden (Oxford, 1951) and a considerable a-mount of his work is available in modern performance editions.

1. Parte Prima / Opera Quinta / Del Sig.^r Archangelo Corelli /
    Ridotta in Concerti a sette parti / Dal Sig.^r Giminiani / Violino
    Principale /

                        D major

    [No. 1]

It. 209
vp, v 2 obl, v 1&
2 conc, vla obl,
vlc obl, bass.
23x32.5cm. 10 st.
WM: 3.
Hand A. Brown.

B flat major

[No. 2]

C major

[No. 3]

F major

[No. 4]

G minor

[No. 5]

A major

[No. 6]

2. Parte Seconda / Opera Quinta / Di Archangelo Corelli / Violino
    Principale /

It. 210
vp, v 2 obl, v 1 &
2 rip, vla obl, vlc
obl, bass.
23.5x32cm. 10 st.
WM: 3 & 14.
Hand A. Brown.

D minor

[No. 7]

E minor

Concerto VIII.

A major

Concerto IX.

F major

Concerto X.

E major

Concerto XI.

D minor

Folia.

GIORNOVICCHI, GIOVANNI

see Jarnović, Ivan Mane

GIOVANNINI, FILIPPO DE

This composer cannot be identified. He may be the Italian musician mentioned by Van der Straeten as a pupil of Leclair,   active in Berlin and London from 1740 to 1782.

C major

1.   Concerto / Del Sig:ʳ / Filippo de Giovannini Romano /   It. 211
                                                                     v 1.
                                                                     23x31cm. 10 st.
                                                                     WM: unclear.
                                                                     Hand ZZ. Black.

GOBBIS, IGNAZIO XAVERIO

This composer cannot be identified.

D major

1.   Sonata a Violino, e Basso / Del / Sig:ʳ Ignazio Gobbis /

It. 212
score.
23x31.5cm. 10 st.
WM: 56.
Hand B. Black.

<u>Another copy</u>. Sonata / del Sig:ʳ Ignazio Gobbis /

It. 213
score.
22x30.5cm. 10 st.
WM: 16.
Hand H² . Brown.

B flat major

2.   Sonata a Violino, e Basso / Del Sig:ʳ Ignazio Gobbis /

It. 214
score.
23x31.5cm. 10 st.
WM: 33.
Hand B. Black.

<u>Another copy</u>. Sonata a Violino e Basso / del Sig:ʳ Ignazio
Gobbis /

It. 215
score.
22.5x31.5cm. 10 st.
WM: 32.
Hand H² . Brown.

Concertos

D major

1. Violino Principale / Concerto / Del Sig:[r] Ignazio Xaverio Gobbis /   It. 216
    vp, v 1 & 2 obl,
    vla, bass.

    23x32cm. 10 st.
    WM: 34.
    Hand B. Black.

Another copy. Concerto / del Sig:[r] Ignazio Xaverio Gobbis /   It. 217
[vp] v 1 & 2 obl,
vla, bass.

Incipit on t. p.   23x32cm. 10 st.
                                                                  WM: 40.
                                                                  Hand H[2]. Brown.

HAIENDEL, FRANCESCO

This composer can probably be identified with Franz Sebastian Haindl, 1727–1812, member of a family of Bavarian musicians. He divided his services as a violinist between the courts of Munich and Innsbruck. His surviving works, all in manuscript, include two masses, an oratorio, two symphonies and a flute concerto. A symphony in G major has been edited by Walter Senn for the Denkmäler der Tonkunst in Österreich, vol. 86.

F major

1. Terzetto / Del Sig.[r] Francesco Haiendel / Basso /   It. 218
    v 1 & 2, bass.

    23x31cm. 10 st.
    WM: 3.
    Hand A. Brown.

G major

2.   Terzetto / Del Sig.ʳ Francesco Haiendel / Basso /

It. 219
v 1 & 2, bass.
23x31.5cm. 10 st.
WM: 3.
Hand A. Brown.

A major

3.   Terzetto / Del Sig.ʳ Francesco Haiendel / Basso /

It. 220
v 1 & 2, bass.
23x31cm. 10 st.
WM: 3.
Hand A. Brown.

HANDEL

The themes for the two duos below have not been found in the works of Georg
Friedrich Händel. Possibly the Francesco Haiendel in the above entry is the
composer to whom they should be attributed.

E flat major

1. Blainte / Lamento amoroso, a Due Violini / Del Sig.ʳ Handel /

It. 221
v 1 & 2.
22.5x31.5cm. 10 st.
WM: 29.
Hand A. Brown.

2. Conforto Amoroso à Due Violini / Del Sig.ʳ Handel / Violino
    Primo /

It. 222
v 1 & 2.
23x31.5cm. 10 st.
WM: 29.
Hand A. Brown.

HAYDN, FRANZ JOSEPH, 1732-1809

1. Nᵒ: VI / Quartetti / Del Sigʳ: Giovanni Haydn / Opera XXXIV /
    Violino Primo /

    Cover title: XLIII / Quartetti / Violino Primo / G: Z: /
    Contains Hoboken III: C 4, E flat 4, B flat 2, A 1, E 1, E flat 5.
    Published Paris, Bérault, 1772, as op. XI.

It. 223
v 1 & 2, vla, vlc.
29.5x22cm. 12 st.
WM: 26.
Hand A⁴. Brown.
(title in another
hand)

2. N:ᵒ VI / Quartetti a Due Violini Viola, e Basso / Del Sigʳ:
    Giovanni Hayden / Violino Primo /

    Cover title: XXXV Quartetti / Violino Primo / G: Z: /
    Contains Hoboken III: 13-18.
    Published Paris, Bailleux, 1777, as op. XXVI.

It. 224
v 1 & 2, vla, vlc.
30.5x22.5cm. 12 st.
WM: 26.
Hand U. Brown.

3. Opera 17 / Violino Primo / Sei Quartetti / A Due Violini, Viola,   It. 225
    e Basso / Del Sig^r: Giuseppe Ha$\ddot{y}$dn /   v 1 & 2, vla, bass.
                                                                               23x32cm. 10 st.
    Contains Hoboken III: 25-30.   WM: 13.
    Published Paris, Sieber, 1773, as op. 17.   Hand VV. Brown.

4. XVIII / Quartetti VI / Del Sig:^{r} Giuseppe Ha$\ddot{y}$dn / Violino Primo /   It. 226
                                                                               v 1 & 2, vla, vlc.
    Contains Hoboken III: 31, 35, 32, 33, 34, 36.   22.5x31cm. 10 st.
    Published Paris, Chevardière, ca. 1774, as op. XX (Hoboken III: WM: 26.
    31, 35, 32, 36, 33, 34)   Hand WW. Black.

    Another copy. Opera 18 / Sei Quartetti / Del Sig.^{r} Giuseppe   It. 227
    Ha$\ddot{y}$dn / Violino Primo /   v 1 & 2, vla, vlc.
                                                                               23x32cm. 10 st.
    Contains Hoboken III: 31, 35, 32, 33, 34, 36.   WM: various.
                                                                               Hand XX. Brown.

5. VI / Quartetti / Opera XXXIII / Del Sig:^{r} Giuseppe Ha$\ddot{y}$dn /   It. 228
    Violino Primo /   v 1 & 2, vla, vlc.
                                                                               30x22cm. 12 st.
    Cover title.   WM: 41.
    Contains Hoboken III: 41, 38, 37, 39, 42, 40.   Hand YY. Brown.
    Published Vienna, Artaria, 1782, as op. 33.

6. La Pasione di / Gesù Cristo / Musica a Quattro / Del Sig^r: It. 229
    Giuseppe Ha$\ddot{y}$dn / Violino Primo /   v 1 & 2, vla, vlc.
                                                                               23x32cm. 10 st.
    Contains Hoboken III: 50-56 (XX B)   WM: 33.
    Published Vienna, Artaria, 1787, as Musica Instrumentale Sopra   Hand U. Brown.
    le Sette Ultime Parole; London, Longman & Broderip, 1787 as A
    Set of Quartetts, Expressive of the Passion of Our Saviour.

7. Violino Primo / N^o: III / Quartetti / Per Due Violini, Viola, e   It. 230
    Basso / Del Sig^r: Giuseppe Haydn / Opera 59: /   v 1 & 2, vla, vlc.
                                                                               22.5x31cm. 10 st.
    Contains Hoboken III: 58, 57, 59.   WM: 45.
    Published Vienna, Artaria (?), 1789/90, as op. 59.   Hand OO. Black.

8. Violino Primo / N^o: III / Quartetti / Per Due Violini, Viola, e   It. 231
    Basso / Del Sig^r: Giuseppe Haydn / Opera 60 /   v 1 & 2, vla, vlc.
                                                                               22.5x31cm. 10 st.
    Contains Hoboken III: 60, 61, 62.   WM: 45.
    Published Vienna, Artaria (?), 1789/90, as op. 60.   Hand OO. Black.

9. Opera 65 / Violino Primo / N^o: III / Quartetti / Per Due Violini,   It. 232
    Viola, e Violoncello / Del Sig^r: Giuseppe Haydn / Libro Primo /   v 1 & 2, vla, vlc.
                                                                               22.5x30cm. 10 st.
    Hoboken III: 65, 68, 67.   WM: 44.
    With this is bound: Opera 65 / No. III / Quartetti ... (Hoboken   Hand QQ & RR.
    III: 66, 63, 64)   Brown & Black.
    Published Offenbach, André, 1791, as op. 65.   (title in Hand OO)

10. Opera 72 / Quartetti / Del Sig:^or Giuseppe Haŷdn / Violino   It. 233
    Primo /   v 1 & 2, vla, vlc.
                                                                         23x32cm. 10 st.
    Contains Hoboken III: 69, 70, 71.   WM: 43.
    Published London, Corri, Dussek, 1795/96, as op. 72.   Hand SS. Brown.

11. Opera 74 / Trè / Quartetti / Per Due Violini, Viola, e Violon-   It. 234
    cello / Del Sig:^r Giuseppe Haŷdn / Violino Primo /   v 1 & 2, vla, vlc.
                                                                         23.5x32.5cm. 10 st.
    Contains Hoboken III: 72, 73, 74.   WM: 42.
    Published Vienna, Artaria, 1796, as op. 74.   Hand TT. Brown.

HELENDAAL (HELLENDAAL), PIETER, 1721-1799

Dutch violinist and composer, born in Rotterdam. He was in Italy as a young
man as a pupil of Tartini. He was in Holland in 1744, living in Amsterdam,
where he published his first set of violin sonatas. From 1752 to the end of his
life he lived in England, chiefly in Cambridge, where he served as organist at
Pembroke and later Peterhouse College. His published works include three sets
of solos for the violin, a set of eight for the cello, and Six Grand Concertos for
violins, Op.3. The latter set appears in a modern critical edition as Vol. I. of
Monumenta Musica Neerlandica (1959). Four of the cello sonatas were edited
as Vol. 41 of the publications of the Vereeniging voor Nederlandsche Muziek-
geschiedenis (1926). Helendaal's most recent editor, Hans Brandts Buys, has
described him as "without doubt the most important composer of Dutch origin in
the 18th century". The Berkeley collection contains nine of his violin sonatas.

C minor

1. No: 10 / Sonata a Violino e Basso / Del / Sig:^r Pietro Helendaal /   It. 235
                                                                         score.
                                                                         22x30cm. 12 st.
                                                                         WM: 19A.
                                                                         Hand A. Black.

<u>D major</u>

2.   No: 4 / Sonata a Violino e Basso / Del / Sig:^r Pietro Helendaal /

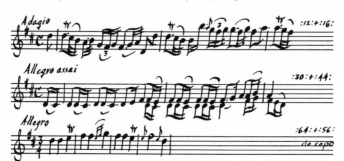

It. 236
score.
22x31.5cm. 10 st.
WM: 63A.
Hand A. Black.

3.   No.: 5 / Sonata a Violino e Basso / Del / Sig:^r Pietro Helendaal /

It. 237
score.
22x30.5cm. 10 st.
WM: 63A.
Hand A. Black.

<u>G minor</u>

4.   No.: 1 / Sonata a Violino e Basso / Del / Sig:^r Pietro Helendaal /

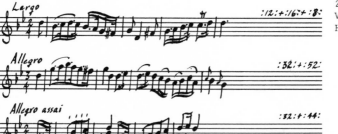

It. 238
score.
22x30.5cm. 8 st.
WM: 63.
Hand A. Black.

A major

5. No: 6 / Sonata a Violino e Basso / Del / Sig:^r Pietro Helendaal /

It. 239
score.
22x30.5cm. 10 st.
WM: 63.
Hand A. Black.

6. No: 7 / Sonata a Violino e Basso / Del / Sig:^r Pietro Helendaal /

It. 240
score.
22x30.5cm. 10 st.
WM: 63.
Hand A. Black.

A minor

7. No: 9 / Sonata a Violino e Basso / Del / Sig:^r Pietro Helendaal /

It. 241
score.
22x30.5cm. 10 st.
WM: 63A.
Hand A. Black.

B flat major

8.   No: 11 / Sonata a Violino e Basso / Del / Sig:^r Pietro Helendaal /

It. 242
score.
22.5x31cm. 10 st.
WM: 63A.
Hand A. Black.

9.   No: 12 / Sonata a Violino e Basso / Del / Sig:^r Pietro Helendaal /

It. 243
score.
22x31.5cm. 10 st.
WM: 63.
Hand A. Brown.

HOFFMEISTER, FRANZ ANTON, 1754-1812

German composer and publisher, born in Rottenburg, Württemberg. He was a
prolific composer of instrumental and vocal music, producing a large quantity of
music for the flute, forty-two string quartets, eighteen string trios, besides
works for piano and strings. His publishing firm, established about 1783, produced numerous first editions of works by Mozart and Beethoven. The two quartets in the Berkeley collection follow a common 18th century practice in deriving
their themes from well known works by other composers, in this case Martini.

1. II / Quartetti / Per due Violini, Violetta, e Basso / Tratti
    dall'opera più rara, e da Migliori / Pessi del Sig^r Martini / E
    disposti dal Sig:^{r} Fran:^{co} Ant:^{o} Hoffmeister / Violino Primo /

It. 244
v 1 & 2, vla, vlc.
23.5x21.5cm. 10 st.
WM: 46.
Hand NN . Brown.

B flat major

No. I.

D major

No. II.

German violinist-composer, born in Munich. He was one of several north European musicians who traveled to Italy to study violin and composition under Tartini. When he returned to Munich in 1762 he became concert master of the court
orchestra. Burney heard him in 1772 and had high praise for his musicianship:
"Holtzbogn has a great hand, a clear tone, and more fire than is usual in one of
the Tartini school ... This performer writes well for his instrument, and played
a very masterly concerto of his own composition." (German Tour, I, p. 173)
None of Holzbogen's music was published and few manuscripts have survived.
There are six trio sonatas in the Berkeley collection.

D major

1. Divertimento / à / Due Violini, e Basso / Del Sig.ʳ Giorgio
    Holzbogn / Basso /

It. 245
v 1 & 2, bass.
23x31cm. 10 st.
WM: 3.
Hand A. Brown.

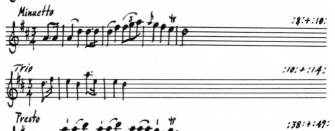

Listed in Breitkopf supplement, 1773, under Trii Flauto traverso
as no. 1 of II Trii da Holzbogen.

E major

2. Divertimento / à / Due Violini, e Basso / Del Sig.ʳ Giorgio
    Holzbogn / Basso /

It. 246
v 1 & 2, bass.
23x31.5cm. 10 st.
WM: 3.
Hand A. Brown.

Listed in Breitkopf supplement, 1773, under Trii per Due Violini
con Basso as no. 1 of IV da Holzbogen.

F major

3.   Divertimento / à / Due Violini, e Basso / Del Sig.^r Giorgio
     Holzbogn / Basso /

It. 247
v 1 & 2, bass.
23x31.5cm. 10 st.
WM: 3.
Hand A.   Brown.

Listed in Breitkopf supplement , 1773, under <u>Trii per Due Violini</u>
<u>con Basso</u> as no. 3 of <u>IV da Holzbogen</u>.

G major

4.   Divertimento / à / Due Violini, e Basso / Del Sig.^r Giorgio
     Holzbogn / Basso /

It. 248
v 1 & 2, bass.
23.5x32cm. 10 st.
WM: 3.
Hand A.   Brown.

Listed in Breitkopf supplement , 1773, under <u>Trii per Due Violini</u>
<u>con Basso</u> as no. 2 of <u>IV da Holzbogen.</u>

A major

5.   Divertimento / à / Due Violini e Basso / Del Sig.ʳ Giorgio
Holzbogn / Basso /

It. 249
v 1 & 2, bass.
23.5x31.5cm. 10 st.
WM: 3.
Hand A.   Brown.

B flat major

6.   Divertimento / à Due Violini, e Basso / Del Sig.ʳ Giorgio
Holzbogn / Basso /

It. 250
v 1 & 2, bass.
23x31.5cm. 10 st.
WM: 3.
Hand A.   Brown.

Listed in Breitkopf supplement , 1773, under Trii per Due Violini
con Basso as no. 4 of IV da Holzbogen.

ILLE CRAM

see Marcelli, Vincenzo

One of the most celebrated violin virtuosos of his day, he was a pupil of Antonio Lolli, and began his career as a performer and teacher in Paris in 1767. In 1779 he left France and began a series of tours which took him to nearly every European country from Ireland to Russia. He wrote some eighteen violin concertos, duos and string quartets; much of his work was published in London, Paris and Berlin. A man of fiery disposition and eccentric behaviour, his career has been amusingly surveyed by Marc Pincherle in Le monde des Virtuoses (Paris, 1961)

E major

1. Concerto / Per Violino con Stromti / Di Monsieur Jarnovič / Violino Principale /

It. 251
vp, v 1 & 2 conc, vla, vlc, oboe 1 & 2, horn 1 & 2. 23x31cm. 10 st. WM: 47. Hand J. Brown.

Listed in Breitkopf supplement, 1781, under Concerti intagliati as I. Conc. da Giornovichi ... Libro I. Berlin.

KLEINKNECHT, JAKOB FRIEDRICH, 1722-1794

Member of a family of musicians active in Ansbach and Ulm from the 17th century, he was a composer and performer on flute and violin. In 1743 he was flutist in the court orchestra at Bayreuth, later becoming violinist and music director. He transferred his activities to Ansbach in 1769. Instrumental music by Kleinknecht, published in London, Paris and Nurnberg, includes concertos, flute sonatas and trio sonatas. Manuscripts of his works are preserved in Brussels, Karlsruhe and Munich.

C major

1.   Sonata â Trê / Del Sig.ʳ Kleingneht / Basso /

It. 252
v 1 & 2, bass.
22.5x30.5cm.10 st.
WM: 32.
Hand A. Brown.

KOŽELUH, LEOPOLD, 1747-1818

Prolific Bohemian composer, he studied composition with his uncle, Jan Antonin Koželuh in Prague in 1765, and pianoforte with F.X. Dušek. He moved to Vienna in 1778, where he spent most of the remainder of his life as a composer and piano teacher. He was Mozart's successor as court composer there. His numerous compositions include operas, ballets, symphonies and piano music.

D major

1.   Sinfonia / A due Violini Viola, e Violoncello / Fagotti due Oboe due Corni / Del Sig:ʳ Leopoldo Kozeluch / Violoncello /

It. 253
v 1 & 2, vla, vlc,
oboe 1 & 2, horn 1
& 2, bassoon.
23.5x32cm. 10 st.
WM: 47.
Hand NN. Black.

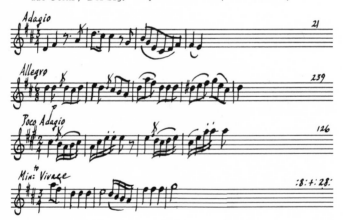

Listed in Breitkopf supplement ,1785, 86 & 87, under <u>Sinfonie</u>
<u>intagliate e stampate</u> as no.1 of <u>III. Sinf. da L. Kozeluch</u> ...
<u>Vol. I Vienna</u>.

<u>D minor</u>

2. Sinfonia / A due Violini Viola, e Violoncello / Fagotti due Oboe
due Corni / Del Sig[r]: Leopoldo Kozeluch / Violoncello /

It. 254

v 1 & 2, vla, vlc,
oboe 1 & 2, horn 1
& 2, bassoon.
23x32cm. 10 st.
WM: 48.
Hand NN. Black.

Listed in Breitkopf supplement ,1785, 86 & 87, under
<u>Sinfonie intagliate e stampate</u> as no.2 of <u>III Sinf. da L.</u>
<u>Kozeluch</u> ... Vol. I Vienna.

F major

3. Sinfonia / A due Violini Viola, e Violoncello / Fagotti due Oboe
   due Corni / Del Sig:ʳ Leopoldo Kozeluch / Violoncello /

It. 255
v 1 & 2, vla, vlc,
oboe 1 & 2, horn 1
& 2, bassoon.
23.5x32cm. 10 st.
WM: 48.
Hand NN. Brown.

Listed in Breitkopf supplement, 1785, 86 & 87, under
Sinfonie intagliate e stampate as no. 3 of III Sinf. da L.
Kozeluch ... Vol. I Vienna.

LOLLI, ANTONIO, 1730-1802

Violinist-composer, born in Bergamo, he was associated with Nardini in 1762
in Stuttgart as a member of the orchestra of the Duke of Württemberg. In 1773
he went to St. Petersburg where he spent five years in the service of the Empress Catherine II. Thereafter he traveled extensively as a virtuoso, in France,
Spain, England, Denmark, until his death at Palermo. His instrumental music,
comprising concertos, sonatas and violin studies, was published in Paris, London and Amsterdam from 1765 to 1785. Lolli was reputed to be a better performer
than musician. Burney observed that "owing to the eccentricity of his style of
composition and execution, he was regarded as a madman by most of the audi-
ence." (History, vol. 4, p. 680) Twelve violin sonatas are found in the Berkeley
collection, grouped as Op. 1 and Op. 2.

1.   Sei Sonate / A Violino, e Basso del Sig:ʳ Antonio Lolli / Opera
    Prima /

<u>D major</u>

Sonata Prima.

Listed in Breitkopf supplement, 1768, as no. 3 of <u>VI Soli di Lolli.</u>

<u>G minor</u>

Sonata Seconda.

Listed in Breitkopf supplement, 1768, as no. 5 of <u>VI Soli di Lolli.</u>

E flat major

Sonata Terza.

Listed in Breitkopf supplement, 1768, as no. 1 of <u>VI Soli di Lolli.</u>

A major

Sonata Quarta.

Listed in Breitkopf supplement, 1768, as no. 6 of <u>VI Soli di Lolli.</u>

G major

Sonata Quinta.

Listed in Breitkopf supplement, 1768, as no. 2 of <u>VI Soli di Lolli</u>.

B flat major

Sonata Sesta.

Listed in Breitkopf supplement, 1768, as no. 4 of <u>VI Soli di Lolli</u>.

2.   Sei Sonate / A Violino, e Basso del Sig:^r Antonio Lolli / Opera
      Seconda /

It. 257
score.
23.5x31.5cm. 10 st.
WM: 49.
Hand J. Brown.

E flat major

Sonata Prima.

C minor

Sonata Seconda.

C major

Sonata Terza.

B flat major

Sonata Quarta.

D major

Sonata Quinta.

G major

Sonata Sesta.

D major

3.   Suonata a Violino e Basso / del Lolli /

It. 258
v & bass.
23x31cm. 10 st.
WM: 24 & 47.
Hand EEE. Brown.

Slightly different version of Opus 1, no.1.

MAGHERINI, GIUSEPPE MARIA, b.ca.1732

Violinist-composer born in the vicinity of Milan. According to Eitner he was
also active in Rome. Eitner gives his birth date as 1752; Fetis and Mendel suggest 1732. He was apparently in London in 1770 for the production of an oratorio, Salomo, of his composition. According to Gerber, six of his trio sonatas
were published in London. There are twelve such works in the Berkeley collection.

D major

1.   Divertimento da Camera / Del Sig.[r] Magherini / Basso /

It. 259
v 1 & 2, bass.
23x31.5cm. 10 st.
WM: 3.
Hand A. Brown.

F major

2. Divertimento da Camera / Del Sig.^r Magherini / Basso /

It. 260
v 1 & 2, bass.
23x31.5cm. 10 st.
WM: 3.
Hand A. Brown.

A major

3. Divertimento da Camera / Del Sig.^r Magherini / Basso /

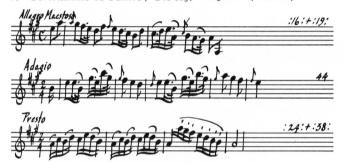

It. 261
v 1 & 2, bass.
23x30.5cm. 10 st.
WM: 3.
Hand A. Brown.

C major

4. Trattenimenti da Camera / Del Sig:^r Giuseppe Magherini / Basso /

It. 262
v 1 & 2, bass.
22x30.5cm. 8 st.
WM: 50.
Hand A. Brown.

D major

5. Trattenimenti da Camera / Del Sig:ʳ Giuseppe M:ª Magherini /
    Violino Primo /

It. 263
v 1 & 2, bass.
22.5x30.5cm. 10 st.
WM: unclear.
Hand B. Black.

6. Trattenimenti da Camera / Del Sig:ʳ Giuseppe Magherini /
    Basso /

It. 264
v 1 & 2, bass.
22x30.5cm. 8 st.
WM: 50.
Hand A. Brown.

7. Trattenimenti da Camera / Del Sig:ʳ Giuseppe Magherini /
    Basso /

It. 265
v 1 & 2, bass.
22x30cm. 8 st.
WM: 50.
Hand A. Brown.

8. Trattenimenti da Camera / Del Sig:r Giuseppe Magherini /
    Basso /

It. 266
v 1 & 2, bass.
22x30cm, 8 st.
WM: 50.
Hand A. Brown.

G major

9. Trattenimenti da Camera / Del Sig:r Giuseppe M:a Magherini /
    Basso /

It. 267
v 1 & 2, bass.
22.5x31cm. 10 st.
WM: unclear.
Hand B. Black.

G minor

10. Trattenimenti da Camera / Del Sig:r Giuseppe Magherini /
     Basso /

It. 268
v 1 & 2, bass.
22x30.5cm. 8 st.
WM: unclear.
Hand A. Brown.

B flat major

11. Trattenimenti da Camera / Del Sig:^r Giuseppe M:^a Magherini /
    Violino Primo /

It. 269
v 1 & 2, bass.
22.5x30.5cm. 10 st.
WM: unclear.
Hand B. Black.

12. Trattenimenti da Camera / Del Sig:^r Giuseppe Magherini /
    Basso /

It. 270
v 1 & 2, bass.
22.5x30.5cm. 8 st.
WM: 50.
Hand A. Brown.

MALDERE, PIERRE VAN, 1724-1768

The most important of three brothers, all violinists and members of the orchestra of Charles of Lorraine in Brussels. His compositions included symphonies, o-vertures, solo sonatas and trios, and were published in Dublin, London, Paris and Lyon. He also composed several operas comiques. The definitive study of this musician has been made by Suzanne Clercx: Pierre van Maldere, Virtuose et Maître des Concerts de Charles de Lorraine. Brussels, 1948.

D major

1.   Sonata a Tre / Del Sig:ʳ Pietro Vanmander / Violino Primo /

It. 271
v 1 & 2, bass.
23x32cm. 10 st.
WM: 51.
Hand A. Brown.

Andante and Fuga illustrated in Clercx, Suzanne. Pierre Van
Maldere, as movements from Sonata I of VI Sonatas for Two
Violins (London, Walsh, 1756)

MANFREDI, FILIPPO, 1729-1780

This musician was born in Lucca, and studied first with Nardini and later with
Tartini.   Returning to serve as violinist at Lucca, he made a number of concert
tours through northern Italy and France in the company of Boccherini.   The two
later traveled to Spain, where Manfredi was appointed first violinist in the chapel of the Infant Don Luis Antonio Jacobo.   He died in Spain in 1780.   A set of
violin sonatas by this composer was published in Paris, and one of his sonatas
appears in Cartier's L'Art de Violon.

<u>B flat major</u>

1. Suonata del Sig:^r Filippo Manfredi Scolora del Sig^r: Pietro
    Nardini /

Caption title.
Transposed version listed in Breitkopf supplement, 1769, as
no. 4 of <u>VI Soli di Filippo Manfredi</u>. <u>Opera I</u>.

MARCELLI, VINCENZO

Nothing is known about the musician who composed the <u>Sinfonia a Sette</u> and the
four trio sonatas following, except that he was from Rimini. He sometimes used
his surname spelled backward as a pseudonym.

<u>D major</u>

1. Basso / Sinfonia a Sette / Del Sig:^r / Vincenzo Marcelli
    Riminese /

Trios
C major

1. Triò / A due Violini, e Basso / Del Sig.ʳ / Vincenzo Marcelli /
    Basso /

It. 274
v 1 & 2, bass.
16x22cm. 10 st.
WM: 52.
Hand MM. Brown.

Incipit on t. p.

2. Triò / A due Violini, è Basso / Del Sigʳ. Illecram / [Basso]

It. 275
v 1 & 2, bass.
16x22cm. 10 st.
WM: 52.
Hand MM. Brown.

D major

3. Triò / A due Violini, è Basso / Del Sigʳ. Illecram / [Basso]

It. 276
v 1 & 2, bass.
16x22cm. 10 st.
WM: 52.
Hand MM. Brown.

Another copy. Trietto A Due Violini 1760. In Roma. Violino 2º /   It. 277
                                                                     v 1 & 2.
Caption title.   16.5x22cm. 10 st.
                                                                     WM: 52.
                                                                     Hand MM. Brown.

G major

4. Triò / A due Violini, è Basso / Del Sig.ʳ / Illecram / [Basso]   It. 278
                                                                         v 1 & 2, bass.
                                                                         16x22cm. 10 st.
                                                                         WM: 52.
                                                                         Hand MM. Brown.

Concertos

A major

1. Violino Primo / Principale / Concerto del / Sig:ʳ / Ille Cram   It. 279
    In Roma / P. G. / R. /   vp.
                                                                     26x38cm. 10 st.
                                                                     WM: 23.
                                                                     Hand MM. Black.

The composer of the following thirteen trio sonatas has not been identified. Both Eitner and Fétis refer to a musician of this name active about 1700 as a composer of church music. Eitner also mentions a musician with the surname Marzola as connected with the cathedral at Ferrara in the mid-18th century.

<u>C major</u>

1.   Trio / Del Sig:^r Pietro Marzola / Basso /

It. 280
v 1 & 2, bass.
22.5x29.5cm. 10 st.
WM: 53.
Hand A. Brown.

2.   Trio / Del Sig^r Pietro Marzola / Basso /

It. 281
v 1 & 2, bass.
22.5x29.5cm. 10 st.
WM: 53.
Hand A. Brown.

3.   Trio / Del Sig.^r Pietro Marzola / Basso /

It. 282
v 1 & 2, bass.
22.5x29.5cm. 10 st.
WM: 53.
Hand A. Brown.

4.   Trio / Del Sig.ʳ Pietro Marzola / Basso /

It. 283
v 1 & 2, bass.
22.5x30.5cm. 10 st.
WM: 53.
Hand A. Brown.

D major

5.   Trio / Del Sig.ʳ Pietro Marzola / Basso /

It. 284
v 1 & 2, bass.
22.5x29cm. 10 st.
WM: 53.
Hand A. Brown.

6.   Trio / Del Sig:ʳ Pietro Marzola / Basso /

It. 285
v 1 & 2, bass.
23x30cm. 10 st.
WM: unclear.
Hand A. Brown.

7.   Trio / Del Sig.ʳ Pietro Marzola / Basso /

It. 286
v 1 & 2, bass.
22.5x29.5cm. 10 st.
WM: 53.
Hand A. Brown.

8.   Trio / Del Sig.^r Pietro Marzola / Basso /

It. 287
v 1 & 2, bass.
23x30cm. 10 st.
WM: 53.
Hand A. Brown.

G major

9.   Trio / Del Sig.^r Pietro Marzola / Basso /

It. 288
v 1 & 2, bass.
22.5x30.5cm. 10 st.
WM: 53.
Hand A. Brown.

10. Trio / Del Sig:^r Pietro Marzola / Basso /

It. 289
v 1 & 2, bass.
22.5x30.5cm. 10 st.
WM: 53.
Hand A. Brown.

11. Trio / Del Sig:^r Pietro Marzola / Basso /

It. 290
v 1 & 2, bass.
22.5x30.5cm. 10 st.
WM: 53.
Hand A. Brown.

12. Trio / Del Sig.^r Pietro Marzola / Basso /

It. 291
v 1 & 2, bass.
22.5x30cm. 10 st.
WM: 53.
Hand A. Brown.

13. Trio / Del Sig^r Pietro Marzola / Basso /

It. 292
v 1 & 2, bass.
23x30cm. 10 st.
WM: 53.
Hand A. Brown.

MENEGHETTI, GIOVANNI BATTISTA

A musician of this name, active in Vincenza, wrote a cantata, L'Arcadia in Brenta, 1757, and other works.

B flat major

1. Sonata à Quattro / del Sig.^r Gio. Batta. Meneghetti / Basso /

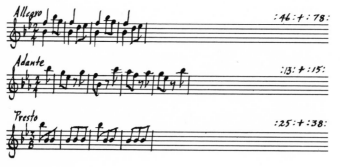

It. 293
v 1, 2 & 3, bass.
22.5x31.5cm. 10 st.
WM: 3.
Hand A. Brown.

see Sguazin, Nicoletto. It.392.

and Anonymous. It.1019.

MORIGI, ANGELO, 1725-1801

This musician was born in Rimini and was a pupil of Tartini and Vallotti in Padua. He became first violinist of the court in Parma in 1766, and director of instrumental music in 1773. Sets of solo violin sonatas, trio sonatas and concertos were published in London from 1751 to 1765. He also wrote a treatise on counterpoint.

C major

1. Sonata / del Sig^r: Angelo Moriggi /   It. 294

score.
23.5x32.5cm. 10 st.
WM: 54.
Hand H^2. Brown.

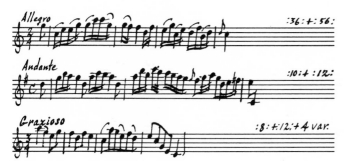

MOSEL, GIOVANNI FELICE, ca. 1754-ca. 1812

Violinist-composer, active chiefly in Florence, he gained his knowledge of the Paduan school of violin performance from his father, who was a pupil of Tartini. The younger Mosel also studied with Nardini, whom he succeeded as first violinist in the chapel of Grand Duke Leopold in Florence in 1793. Duos by Mosel were published in Paris, Amsterdam and Venice.

1.   Duetti VI / Del Sig:ʳ Felice Mosel / Violino Primo /

It. 295
v 1.
23.5x31.5cm. 10 st.
WM: various.
Hand FFF. Brown.

C major

N.º I.

B flat major

N.º II.

D major

N.º III.

E flat major

N:º IV.

F major

N:º V.

G major

N:º VI.

1. Tre Quartetti / per / Due Violini Viola e Basso / del Sig:ʳ
    Mozart / Violino Primo /

    K. 575, 589, 590.
    Published Vienna, Artaria, 1791.

MYSLIVEČEK, JOSEF, 1737-1781

Best known as a composer of opera, he was born near Prague and began his musical training there. In 1763 he was in Venice studying opera composition with
Pescetti. His first opera, Medea, was produced in Parma in 1764, and by 1780
some twenty-five operatic works had been performed in the principal opera houses
of Italy. He also wrote considerable instrumental music, including overtures,
quartets, orchestral trios and symphonies, published in London, Paris and Amsterdam.

E flat major

1. Sonata a Tre / Del Sig:ʳ Giuseppe Misliwezek / Violino Primo /

Listed in Breitkopf supplement, 1767, as no. 4 of VI Trii di
Mislewecek.

Violinist-composer and leading representative of the Tartini school, he began
his studies with Tartini at the age of twelve. From 1740 he was a violinist and
teacher in Livorno, his birthplace. After a short visit to Dresden, he returned
to Italy, and in 1762 was appointed to the court orchestra of the Duke of Württemberg at Stuttgart under Jommelli. He was in Padua again in May 1769. In
the same year he was appointed concert master to the Grand Duke Leopold in
Florence, where he remained to the end of his career. As a composer Nardini
confined himself to instrumental music, much of which was published in London
and Amsterdam. Manuscript copies of his music are found in many European libraries. In the Berkeley collection are seventeen violin sonatas and six violin
concertos.

1. Cinque Sonate Per Violino, e Basso Solo / Del Sig^r: Pietro   It. 298
    Nardini /   score.
                                                                       23x31.5cm. 10 st.
                          G major   WM: 25.
                                                                       Hand O. Black.

Sonata I.

Listed by Pfäfflin as no.5 of <u>Dodici Sonate a Violino solo con</u>
<u>suo Basso</u> [manuscript]

                          D major

Sonata II.

Listed by Pfäfflin as no.2 of <u>VII Sonates avec les Adagios brodés</u>.
(Paris, Décombe)

<u>See also It.302.</u>

G minor

Sonata III.

Listed by Pfäfflin as no. 3 of <u>Dodici Sonate a Violino solo con suo Basso</u> [manuscript]

A major

Sonata IV.

G major

Sonata V.

Listed by Pfäfflin as one of 19 mss. sonatas in the library of the
Gesellschaft der Musikfreunde, Vienna.

Another copy. Sonatas I-IV. See It. 1020.

Sonatas

C major

1. Sonata a Violino, e Basso / Del / Sig:^r Pietro Nardini /

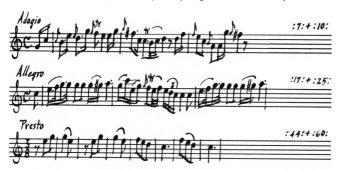

It. 299
score.
23x32cm. 10 st.
WM: 56.
Hand B. Black.

Listed by Pfäfflin as no. 4 of Six Solos for a Violin with a Bass
for the Harpsichord or Violoncello. (London, Walsh, ca. 1760)

Another copy. Sonata a Violino, e Basso del Sig:^r Pietro
Nardini /

Caption title.

It. 300
score.
22.5x30cm. 8 st.
WM: unclear.
Hand H. Brown.

2. Sonata à Violino e Basso / Del Sig^r: / Pietro Nazari / di /
Venezia /

It. 301
score.
23.5x32.5cm. 10 st.
WM: unclear.
Hand GGG. Brown.

Caption title: Sonata à Violino e Basso Del / Sig^r. Pietro
Nardini Celebre Profes.^or / di Violino / (in Hand F)
Signed: Pro:^ne An? Br:^ti /
Larghetto for "violino con sordino corno inglese e basso"
(fragment) on last page.

<u>D major</u>

3.   Sonata a Violino, e Basso / Del Sig:^r / Pietro Nardini /   It. 302

Listed by Pfäfflin as no. 2 of <u>VII Sonates avec les Adagios brodés</u>.
(Paris, Décombe)

See also It. 298.

It. 302
score.
22.5x31.5cm. 12 st.
WM: 40.
Hand II. Brown.
(title in Hand B)

4.   Sonata a Violino, e Basso / Del / Sig:^r Pietro Nardini /   It. 303

Listed by Pfäfflin as no. 5 of <u>Six Solos for a Violin with a Bass
for the Harpsichord or Violoncello</u>. (London, Walsh, ca. 1760)

Another copy. Suonata / A Violino e Basso / Del Sig^r: Pietro
Nardini /

It. 303
score.
23x28cm. - 10 st.
WM: 56.
Hand B. Black.

It. 304
score.
23x32.5cm. 10 st.
WM: 35.
Hand II. Brown.

5.   Sonata a Violino, e Basso / Del / Sig:ʳ Pietro Nardini /

It. 305

score.
23x32cm. 10 st.
WM: 29.
Hand A. Brown.

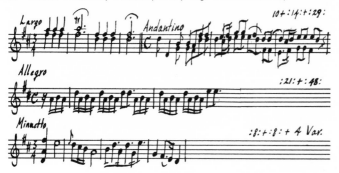

6.   Sonata à violino Solo / e Basso / Del Sig:ʳ Pietro Nardini /
     Nᴼ: 15.

It. 306

score.
22x29.5cm. 10 st.
WM: unclear.
Hand HHH. Brown.

Incipit on t.p.

E flat major

7.   Sonata a Violino, e Basso / Del Sig:ʳ Pietro Nardini /

It. 307

score.
22.5x31.5cm. 12 st.
WM: 40.
Hand II. Brown.
(title in Hand B)

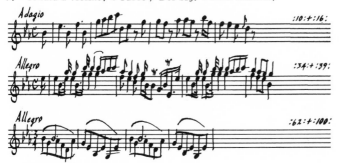

Listed by Pfäfflin as no.1 of VII Sonates avec les Adagios brodés.
(Paris, Décombe)

E major

8.   Sonata a Violino, e Basso / Del / Sig:^r Pietro Nardini /

It. 308
score.
23.5x32cm. 10 st.
WM: 29.
Hand A. Brown.

Listed by Pfäfflin as no.3 of VII Sonates avec les Adagios brodés.
(Paris, Décombe)
Embellished version of Adagio: It. 1003:1.

G major

9.   Sonata a Violino / e Basso / Del Sig^r: Pietro Nardini /
     N^o: 16.

It. 309
score.
23.5x29.5cm. 10 st.
WM: 57.
Hand HHH. Brown.

A major

10. Sonata a Violino e Basso / Del Sig:^r Pietro Nardini /

It. 310
score.
23.5x32cm. 12 st.
Hand II. Brown.
(title in Hand B)

B flat major

11. Sonata a Violino, e Basso / Del / Sig:^{r} Pietro Nardini /

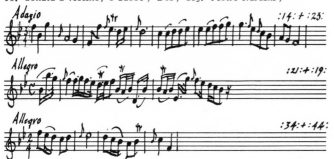

It. 311
score.
23x31.5cm. 10 st.
WM: 98.
Hand B. Black.

Listed by Pfäfflin as no. 6 of <u>Six Solos for a Violin with a Bass</u>
<u>for the Harpsichord or Violoncello</u>. (London, Walsh, ca. 1760)

<u>Another copy</u>. N^o: 1. Suonata a Violino e Basso / Del Sig^r:
Pietro Nardini /

It. 312
score.
22.5x31.5cm. 10 st.
WM: 59.
Hand II. Brown.

12. Sonata a Violino, e Basso / Del / Sig^r: Pietro Nardini /

It. 313
score.
23.5x31.5cm. 10 st.
WM: 98.
Hand B. Black.

<u>Another copy</u>. N^o: 2 / Suonata / A Violino e Basso / Del Sig^r:
Pietro Nardini /

It. 314
score.
22.5x31.5cm. 10 st.
WM: 59.
Hand II. Brown.

Concertos

C major

1. Violino Principale / Concerto / Del Signor Pietro Nardini /
   con Violini Obligati Viola e Basso / Violini Ripieno /

It. 315
vp, v 1 & 2 obl,
vla, bass.
23x31.5cm. 10 st.
WM: 59.
Hand II. Brown.

D major

2. Violino Principale / Concerto / Del Sig.ʳ Pietro Nardini /

It. 316
vp, v 1 & 2 obl,
vla, vlc obl.
22.5x30cm. 10 st.
WM: 63A.
Hand A. Brown.

3. Violino Principale / Concerto / Del Sig.ʳ Pietro Nardini /

It. 317
vp, v 1 & 2 obl,
vla [bass]
24x32cm. 10 st.
WM: 36.
Hand A. Brown.

4. Violino Principale / Concerto / Del Sig.^r Pietro Nardini /

It. 318
vp, v 1 & 2 obl,
bass.
22x30cm. 10 st.
WM: 15.
Hand A. Brown.

5. Violino Principale / Concerto / Del Sig.^r Pietro Nardini /

It. 319
vp, v 1 & 2 obl,
vla, bass.
23.5x32cm. 10 st.
WM: 36.
Hand A. Brown.

G major

6. Violino Principale / Concerto / Del Sig.^r Pietro Nardini /

It. 320
vp, v 1 & 2 obl,
vla, bass.
23.5x32.5cm. 10 st.
WM: 36.
Hand A. Brown.

A pupil of Tartini, and violinist in St. Mark's in Venice around 1780.

C major

1. Suonata / A Violino e Basso / Del Sig^r: Antonio Nazari /

It. 321
score.
22.5x31.5cm. 10 st.
WM: 59.
Hand II. Brown.

E flat major

2. Suonata / A Violino e Basso / Del Sig^r: Antonio Nazari /

It. 322
score.
22.5x31cm. 10 st.
WM: 59.
Hand II. Brown.

Concertos

F major

1. Violino Principale / Concerto / Del Signor Antonio Nazari /

It. 323
vp, v 1 & 2 obl,
vla, bass.
22.5x31.5cm. 10 st.
WM: 59 & 3.
Hand II. Brown.

A major

2. Violino Principalle / Conserto / Del Sig[r]: Antonio Nazari /

It. 324
vp, v 1 & 2 obl,
vla, bass.
22.5x31.5cm. 10 st.
WM: 59.
Hand II. Brown.

NAZARI, PIETRO

see It. 301.

OGLIO, DOMENICO DALL', ca. 1700-1764

Violinist-composer, probably born in Padua and a pupil of Tartini, he was appointed as violinist in the Cappella of St. Anthony in Padua on Dec. 29, 1732.
In 1735 he was granted a leave to visit Russia, where he remained for twenty-
nine years in the service of the Russian court. He made periodic request for
extensions of his leave from Padua until 1743 when he resigned his position
there. He was killed in an accident during his return trip to Italy in 1764.
Twelve solo violin sonatas were published in Amsterdam in 1738; another set of
twelve appeared posthumously in Venice in 1778. Six symphonies appeared in
Paris in 1753. Manuscript instrumental music by Dall'Oglio is found in libraries
in Bologna, Venice, Vienna and Uppsala. The twenty-two violin sonatas and
seventeen concertos in the Berkeley collection make it one of the richest sources
of the work of this composer. Twelve of the twenty-two sonatas are probably
copies from the Amsterdam edition, whose title reads XII Sonate a Violino e Violoncello o Cimbalo.

C major

1. Sonata a Violino, e Basso Del Sig.[r] Domenico Dall' Oglio /

It. 325
score.
23x32.5cm. 10 st.
WM: 3.
Hand A. Black.

Caption title.

2. Sonata a Violino, e Violoncello, o Cimbalo. Del Sig^r. Dom^{co}. dall' Oglio /

It. 326
score.
23x31.5cm. 10 st.
WM: 73.
Hand R. Black.

Caption title.
Published as no. 7 of XII Sonate ... Opera Prima. (Amsterdam, Witvogel, 1738)

3. Sonata a Violino, e Violoncello / o Cimbalo / Del Sig^r. Domenico Dall' Oglio /

It. 327
score.
22.5x31.5cm. 10 st.
WM: unclear.
Hand R. Black.

Published (with an additional Adagio) as no. 1 of XII Sonate ... Opera Prima. (Amsterdam, Witvogel, 1738)

4. Sonata à Violino, é Basso del Sig.^r Domenico Dall' Oglio /

It. 328
score.
23x32.5cm. 10 st.
WM: 3.
Hand A. Black.

Caption title.

5. Sonata a Violino, e Basso del Sig:^r Domenico dall' Oglio /

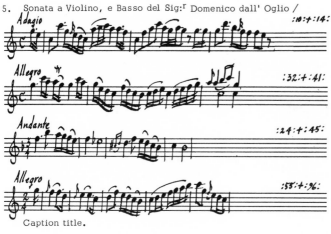

It. 329
score.
23.5x32.5cm. 10 st.
WM: 3.
Hand A. Black.

Caption title.

D major

6. Sonata à Violino, e Basso / Del / Sig:^r Domenico Dall' Oglio /

It. 330
score.
22x30cm. 10 st.
WM: unclear.
Hand A. Brown.

Published as no. 2 of XII Sonate ... Opera Prima. (Amsterdam, Witvogel, 1738)

7.   Sonata a Violino, e Basso / Del / Sig.^r Domenico dall' Oglio /

It. 331
score.
23x32.5cm. 10 st.
WM: 3.
Hand A. Brown.

Possibly by Tartini. Listed by Brainard as D. 17.

E flat major

8.   Sonata á Violino, e Basso / Del / Sig:^r Domenico Dall' Oglio /

It. 332
score.
23x31.5cm. 10 st.
WM: unclear.
Hand A. Brown.

Published as no. 8 of XII Sonate ... Opera Prima. (Amsterdam,
Witvogel, 1738)

9.   Sonata a Violino, e Basso / Del / Sig.^r Domenico dall' Oglio /

It. 333
score.
23x32cm. 10 st.
WM: 3.
Hand A. Brown.

E major

10. Sonata a Violino, e Basso / Del / Sig:^r Domenico dall' Oglio /

It. 334
score.
23x32cm. 10 st.
WM: 3.
Hand A. Brown.

E minor

11. Sonata a Violino, e / Violoncello / o Cembalo / Del / Sig^r.
Dom^{co} dall' Oglio /

It. 335
score.
22.5x32cm. 10 st.
WM: 73.
Hand R. Brown.

Published as no. 12 of XII Sonate ... Opera Prima. (Amsterdam,
Witvogel, 1738)

F major

12. Sonata a Violino, e Basso / Del / Sig:^r Domenico Dall' Oglio /

It. 336
score.
22x30cm. 10 st.
WM: unclear.
Hand A. Black.

Published as no. 5 of XII Sonate ... Opera Prima. (Amsterdam,
Witvogel, 1738)

G major

13. Sonata a Violino, e / Violoncello, o / Cembalo / Del / Sig^r.
   Dom^{co} dall' Oglio /

It. 337
score.
23x32cm. 10 st.
WM: unclear.
Hand R. Brown.

Published (with an additional Largo) as no. 11 of XII Sonate ...
Opera Prima. (Amsterdam, Witvogel, 1738)

14. Sonata a Violino, e / Violoncello, o / Cimbalo / Del / Sig^r.
   Dom^{co} dall' Oglio /

It. 338
score.
23x32cm. 10 st.
WM: unclear.
Hand R. Brown.

Published (with an additional Andante) as no. 6 of XII Sonate ...
Opera Prima. (Amsterdam, Witvogel, 1738)

15. Sonata a Violino, e Basso / Del / Sig.^r Domenico dall' Oglio /

It. 339
score.
23x33cm. 10 st.
WM: 3.
Hand A. Brown.

16. Sonata à Violino, e Basso del Sig.^r Domenico Dall' Oglio /

It. 340
score.
23.5x32.5cm. 10 st.
WM: 3.
Hand A. Black.

Caption title.

Another copy. Sonata a Violino e Basso / Del / Sig:^r Giuseppe
Tartini / See It. 753.

G minor

17. Sonata a Violino, e Violoncello, o Cimbalo del Sig^r. Dom^{co}
Dall' Oglio /

It. 341
score.
22x32cm. 10 st.
WM: unclear.
Hand R. Black.

Caption title.
Published as no. 4 of <u>XII Sonate</u> ... <u>Opera Prima.</u> (Amsterdam,
Witvogel, 1738)

A major

18. Sonata a Violino, e Basso del Sig.^{r} Domenico dall' Oglio /

It. 342
score.
23.5x32.5cm. 10 st.
WM: 3.
Hand A. Black.

Caption title.

19. Sonata a Violino, e Basso / Del / Sig:ʳ Domenico Dall' Oglio /   It. 343
score.
21.5x29.5cm. 10 st.
WM: unclear.
Hand A. Black.

Published (with an additional Largo-Allegro) as no. 3 of XII
Sonate ... Opera Prima. (Amsterdam, Witvogel, 1738)

A minor

20. Sonata a Violino, e / Violoncello / o Cembalo / Del / Sigʳ.   It. 344
Domᶜᵒ dall' Oglio /
score.
22.5x32cm. 10 st.
WM: unclear.
Hand R. Brown.

Published as no. 9 of XII Sonate ... Opera Prima. (Amsterdam,
Witvogel, 1738)

B flat major

21. Sonata / à / Violino è Basso / Del Sigʳ / Domenico Dall' Oglio /   It. 345
score.
23x30.5cm. 10 st.
WM: unclear.
Hand JJJ. Brown.

Incipit on t. p.
Published as no. 10 of XII Sonate ... Opera Prima. (Amsterdam,
Witvogel, 1738)

22. Sonata a Violino Solo del Sig:^r Domenico dall' Oglio /

Caption title.

It. 346

score.
23x32cm. 10 st.
WM: unclear.
Hand B[1]. Brown.

Concertos

C major

1. Violino Principale / Concerto / Del Sig.^r Domenico Dall' Oglio /

It. 347

vp, v 1 & 2 obl,
vla, vlc obl.
22.5x32cm. 10 st.
WM: 56.
Hand A. Brown.

2. Violino Principale / Concerto / Del Sig:^r Domenico Dall' Oglio /

It. 348

vp, v 1 & 2 obl,
vla, vlc obl.
22.5x32cm. 10 st.
WM: 56.
Hand A.

Another copy. Violino Principale / Concerto / Del Sig:^r
Domenico Dall' Oglio /

It. 349
vp, v 1 & 2 obl,
vla, vlc obl.
22.5x31.5cm. 10 st.
WM: 56.
Hand A. Brown.

D major

3. Violino Principale / Concerto / Del Sig.^r Domenico Dall' Oglio /

It. 350
vp, v 1 & 2 obl,
vla, vlc obl.
22.5x32cm. 10 st.
WM: 56.
Hand A. Brown.

4. Violino Principale / Concerto / Del Sig:^r Domenico Dall' Oglio /

It. 351
vp, v 1 & 2 obl,
vla, vlc obl.
22.5x31.5cm. 10 st.
WM: 56.
Hand A. Brown.

5.   Violino Principale / Concerto / Del Sig.^r Domenico Dall' Oglio /   It. 352

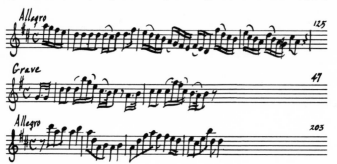

vp, v 1 & 2 obl,
vla, vlc obl.
22.5x31.5cm. 10 st.
WM: 56.
Hand A. Brown.

E major

6.   Violino Principale / Concerto / Del Sig:^r Domenico Dall' Oglio /   It. 353

vp, v 1 & 2 obl,
vla, vlc obl.
22.5x32.5cm. 10 st.
WM: 5 & 2.
Hand B. Black.

Another copy. Violino Principale / Del Sig^r: Domenico Dal'   It. 354
Oglio /

Incipit on t. p.

vp, v 1 & 2 obl,
vla, vlc obl.
23x32cm. 10 st.
WM: 6 & 16.
Hand O. Brown.

F major

7.   Violino Principale / Concerto / Del Sig:^r Domenico Dall' Oglio /   It. 355

vp, v 1 & 2 obl,
vla, vlc obl.
22.5x31cm. 10 st.
WM: 56.
Hand A. Brown.

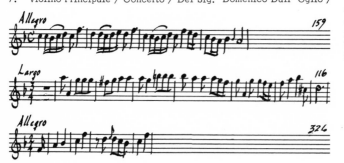

8.   Violino Principale / Concerto / Del Sig.^{r} Domenico Dall' Oglio /

It. 356
vp, v 1 & 2 obl,
vla, vlc obl.
23x32cm. 10 st.
WM: 56 & 31.
Hand A. Brown.

Another copy. Violino Principale / Concerto / Del Sig.^{r}
Pasqualino Bini / See It. 95.

9.   Violino Principale / Concerto / Del Sig.^{r} Domenico Dall' Oglio /

It. 357
vp, v 1 & 2 obl,
vla, vlc obl.
22.5x31.5cm. 10 st.
WM: 56.
Hand A. Brown.

10. Violino Principale / Concerto / Del Sig.^{r} Domenico Dall' Oglio /

It. 358
vp, v 1 & 2 obl,
vla, vlc obl.
23x32cm. 10 st.
WM: 31.
Hand A. Black.

<u>G major</u>

11. Violino Principale / Concerto / Del Sig:ʳ Domenico Dall' Oglio /

It. 359
vp, v 1 & 2 obl,
vla, vlc obl.
22.5x31.5cm. 10 st.
WM: 56.
Hand A. Brown.

12. Violino Principale / Concerto / Del Sig:ʳ Domenico Dall' Oglio /

It. 360
vp, v 1 & 2 obl,
vla, vlc obl.
22.5x31.5cm. 10 st.
WM: 56.
Hand A. Brown.

13. Violino Principale / Concerto / Del Sig:ʳ Domenico Dall' Oglio /

It. 361
vp, v 1 & 2 obl,
vla, vlc obl.
22.5x32cm. 10 st.
WM: 56.
Hand A. Brown.

A major

14. Violino Principale / Concerto / Del Sig.^r Domenico Dall' Oglio /

It. 362
vp, v 1 & 2 obl,
vla, vlc obl.
22.5x32cm. 10 st.
WM: 31 & 56.
Hand A. Brown.

15. Violino Principale / Concerto / Del Sig.^r Domenico Dall' Oglio /

It. 363
vp, v 1 & 2 obl,
vla, vlc obl.
22.5x32cm. 10 st.
WM: 56.
Hand A. Brown.

B flat major

16. Violino Principale / Concerto / Del Sig:^r Domenico Dall' Oglio /

It. 364
vp, v 1 & 2 obl,
vla, vlc obl.
23x32cm. 10 st.
WM: 31 & 56.
Hand A. Brown.

17. Violino Principale / Concerto / Del Sig:ʳ Domenico Dall' Oglio /

It. 365
vp, v 1 & 2 obl,
vla, vlc obl.
22.5x31.5cm. 10 st.
WM: 56.
Hand A. Brown.

ORSINI, GAETANO, fl. 1730

Eitner has identified this musician with an alto singer at the court chapel in
Vienna, who died in 1750 at the age of 83. Six trio sonatas, Op. 1, were pub-
lished in Venice, ca. 1730; a copy of this set is in the British Museum. An
Op. 7, also trio sonatas, is in the collection of the Gesellschaft für Musik-
freunde in Vienna, and the six trios in Berkeley are duplicated in a set at the
Bibliothèque Nationale in Paris.

1. N:º VI / Trio / A Due Violini e Basso / Del Sig:ʳ Gaetano   It. 366
    Orsini / Violino Primo /   v 1 & 2, vlc.
                                                                       23.5x32cm. 10 st.
                                                                       WM: 25.
                          B flat major   Hand PP. Brown.

    Trio I.

E flat major

Trio II.

A flat major

Trio III.

C major

Trio IV.

G major

Trio V.

D major

Trio VI.

Published as <u>Sei Trio per due violini e violoncello</u> ... <u>Opera
Prima.</u> (Venezia, Zatta, ca. 1730).
Themes listed in <u>Catalogue du Fonds de Musique Ancienne de
la Bibliotheque Nationale</u>, par I. Ecorcheville.

PAVONA, PIETRO ALESSANDRO, 1729-1786

An organist and composer of sacred music, he was born in Palmanova, studied
organ and composition with Bartolomeo Cordans, chapel master at Udine. In
1759 he became organist at the cathedral in Cividale where he remained for the
rest of his life. A collection of his four-voice masses was published in 1770.
Instrumental music by this composer is not known, apart from the three trio sonatas below.

D major

1. Trio / Del Sig:^r Pietro Pavona / Basso /

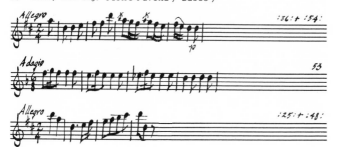

It. 367
v 1 & 2, bass.
22.5x32cm. 10 st.
WM: 4 & 60.
Hand A. Brown.

E minor

2. Trio / Del Sig:^r Pietro Pavona / Basso /

It. 368
v 1 & 2, bass.
23x32cm. 10 st.
WM: 60.
Hand A. Brown.

A major

3. Trio / Del Sig:^r Pietro Pavona / Basso /

It. 369
v 1 & 2, bass.
22.5x32cm. 10 st.
WM: 60 & 28.
Hand A. Brown.

One of the leading violinists, composers and teachers of his day, he was born in Turin. He is said to have studied with Somis and Tartini, but his only known teacher was V. Ciampi in composition (Rome, 1749-1750). He was appointed violinist in the court at Turin in 1748, and returned there in 1770 as first violinist, after an extended period of travel. His foreign tours took him to Paris, London and St. Petersburg. Viotti was one of his pupils. He was a prolific composer of operas, ballets and instrumental music. His published works include three sets of violin sonatas, numerous duos, trios, quartets, quintets and twelve symphonies. His biographer, Elsa Zschinsky-Troxler, provides a thematic catalog and cites examples of Pugnani's work in some thirty-two European libraries.

D major

1.   Suonata / A Violino e Basso / Del Sig.ʳ Gaetano Pugnani /

It. 370
score.
23x32cm. 10 st.
WM: 87.
Hand II. Brown.

Trios

C major

1.   Trio / Del Sig.ʳ Gaetano Pugnani / Basso /

It. 371
v 1 & 2, bass.
23x32cm. 10 st.
WM: 4.
Hand A. Brown.

Listed by Zschinsky-Troxler as the first 3 movements of Nr. 52, published in London & Paris as one of six trios, op.1 (1754).

2.   Trio / Del Sig.ʳ Gaetano Pugnani / Basso /

It. 372
v 1& 2, bass.
23x32cm. 10 st.
WM: 4.
Hand A. Brown.

Listed by Zschinsky-Troxler as Nr. 49, published in London &
Paris as one of six trios, op. 1 (1754).

F major

3.   Trio / Del Sig.ʳ Gaetano Pugnani / Basso /

It. 373
v 1& 2, bass.
23x32cm. 10 st.
WM: 4.
Hand A. Brown.

Listed by Zschinsky-Troxler as Nr. 48, published in London &
Paris as one of six trios, op. 1 (1754).

G major

4.   Trio / Del Sig.ʳ Gaetano Pugnani / Basso /

It. 374
v 1& 2, bass.
23x32cm. 10 st.
WM: 4.
Hand A. Brown.

Listed by Zschinsky-Troxler as Nr. 47, published in London &
Paris as one of six trios, op. 1 (1754).

A major

5. Trio / Del Sig.¹ Gaetano Pugnani / Basso /

It. 375
v 1 & 2, bass.
23x32cm. 10 st.
WM: 4.
Hand A. Brown.

Listed by Zschinsky-Troxler as Nr. 51, published in London &
Paris as one of six trios, op. 1 (1754).

B flat major

6. Trio / Del Sig.ʳ Gaetano Pugnani / Basso /

It. 376
v 1 & 2, bass.
23x32cm. 10 st.
WM: 4.
Hand A. Brown.

Listed by Zschinsky-Troxler as Nr. 50, published in London &
Paris as one of six trios, op. 1 (1754).

RAIMONDI, IGNAZIO, ca. 1733-1813

Violinist-composer, pupil of Barbella, born in Naples. He was active in concert life in Amsterdam from about 1760, later in Paris, and finally established
himself in London where he remained as a performer and teacher to the end of
his life. He composed much instrumental music: duos, trios, quartets, concertos and symphonies were published in Amsterdam, Berlin and London. The
twelve violin sonatas in the Berkeley collection are designated as his Opus 3
and Opus 4.

1. No. Sei Suonate / Di Ignazio Raimondi / Opera Terza /

It. 377
score.
23.5x32.5cm. 10 st.
WM: 61.
Hand BBB? Black.

B flat major

Sonata I.

D major

Sonata II.

F major

Sonata III.

E flat major

Sonata IV.

A major

Sonata V.

G major

Sonata VI.

2.   No. Sei Suonate / Di Ignazio Raimondi / Opera Sesta /

It. 378
score.
23.5x32.5cm. 10 st.
WM: 61.
Hand BBB. Black.

G major

Sonata I.

D major

Sonata II.

B flat major

Sonata III.

C major

Sonata IV.

D major

Sonata V.

E major

Sonata VI.

In all probability the concerto attributed to Monsieur San Giorgio, below, is the work of Le Chevalier de Saint-Georges, an almost legendary figure in late 18th-century France. Adventurer, swordsman, involved in political intrigue, he was also a skilled violinist and composer. He studied violin with Leclair and composition with Gossec, and his concertos, quartets, sonatas and symphonies were published in Paris and London. He was the subject of a four-volume fictional biography by Roger de Beauvoir (Paris, 1840). Lionel de la Laurencie provides an extended account of his life and work in L'École Française de Violon (Paris, 1923).

G major

1. Concerto / Per Violino con Stromti / Di Monsieur San Giorgio / Violino Principale /

It. 379
vp, v 1 & 2 conc,
vla, vlc, oboe 1
& 2, horn 1 & 2.
23x31.5cm. 10 st.
WM: 47.
Hand J. Brown.

SAMMARTINI, GIOVANNI BATTISTA, 1698-1775

Organist and composer, born in Milan. He was chapel master from 1730 to 1770 of Santa Maria Maddalena in Milan, and director of the orchestra for the Governor-General of Lombardy. He was the teacher of Gluck and an important figure in the development of the pre-classic instrumental style. A prolific composer of instrumental music, his work is frequently confused with that of his brother, Giuseppe, who was active in London. Eight trio sonatas are in the Berkeley collection.

G major

1. Sonata a 3 / Del Sig:ʳ Gio: Batta: S. Martino / Violino Pmo: /

It. 380
v 1 & 2, bass.
22.5x31.5cm. 10 st.
WM: 62.
Hand B. Black.

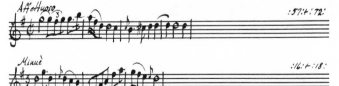

Listed by Refardt as kr. IV 292 Nr. 1. (London, Walsh, 1756. op. 5 no. 2)

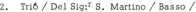

C major

2.   Trio / Del Sig.ʳ S. Martino / Basso /

It. 381
v l & 2. bass.
22.5x31cm. 8 st.
WM: 16.
Hand A. Brown.

Listed by Refardt as kr.IV 294 Nr.2.

D major

3.   Trio / Del Sig.ʳ S. Martino / Basso /

It. 382
v l & 2, bass.
22.5x30.5cm. 8 st.
WM: 16.
Hand A. Brown.

E flat major

4.   Trio / Del Sig.ʳ S. Martino / Basso /

It. 383
v l & 2, bass.
22.5x30.5cm. 8 st.
WM: 16.
Hand A. Brown.

E major

5.   Trio / Del Sig.ʳ S. Martino / Basso /

It. 384
v l & 2, bass.
22.5x30.5cm. 8 st.
WM: 16.
Hand A. Brown.

Listed by Refardt as kr.IV 293 Nr.4. (London, Walsh, 1756.
op.5 no.4)

G major

6. Trið / Del Sig:ʳ S. Martino / Basso /

It. 385
v 1 & 2, bass.
23x32cm. 8 st.
WM: 16 & 4.
Hand A. Brown.

Transposed version (A major) listed by Refardt as kr.IV 292
Nr.4. (London, Walsh, 1756. op.5 no.5)

G minor

7. Trið / Del Sig:ʳ S. Martino / Basso /

It. 386
v 1 & 2, bass.
23.5x32cm. 8 st.
WM: 16 & 4.
Hand A. Brown.

B flat major

8. Trið / Del Sig:ʳ S. Martino / Basso /

It. 387
v 1 & 2, bass.
22x30.5cm. 10 st.
WM: 4.
Hand A. Brown.

Listed by Refardt as kr.IV 292 Nr.2.(Attributed to Giuseppe
Sammartini)

SAN GIORGIO

see Saint Georges, Joseph Bologne

Probably Bernhard Scheff, who was sent to study with Tartini by Carl August
Friedrich, Fürst zu Waldeck, about 1740. cf. Rouvel, Diether. <u>Zur Geschichte
der Musik am Fürstlich Waldeckschen Hofe zu Arolsen</u>. Regensburg, 1962.
p.89-90, 251-260.

G major

1. Sonata / à Violino, e Basso / Del Sig:^r Bernardo Schelf /

It. 388
score.
23x31.5cm. 10 st.
WM: unclear.
Hand LLL. Brown.

Concertos

A major

1. Violino Principale / Concerto / Del Sig:^r Bernardo Schelff /

It. 389
vp, v 1 & 2 obl,
vla, bass.
22.5x31cm. 10 st.
WM: 22.
Hand A. Brown.

<u>Another copy</u>. Violino Principale / Concerto / Del Sig:^r
Bernardo Schelff /

Incipit on t.p.

It. 390
vp, v 1 & 2 obl,
vla, bass.
23.5x30.5cm. 10 st.
WM: 14.
Hand MMM. Brown.

The identity of this musician has not been established, but it is possible that
the name on the violin sonata below is a corruption of Carlo Chiabrano (Charles
Chabran), a nephew and pupil of Somis at Turin.   He went to Paris in 1751,
later to London, and had a set of violin sonatas published in both cities.

E major

1.   Sonata a Violino, e Basso / Di Monsieur Carlo Sciabra   It. 391
     Francese /   score.
                                                                    23x32.5cm. 10 st.
                                                                    WM: 56.
                                                                    Hand B. Black.

SGUAZIN, NICOLETTO

This composer has not been identified.   A manuscript copy of the Sei divertimenti of the Berkeley collection appears in the Marciana in Venice, with the
composer's name given as Mestrino.   There seems no reason to identify Sguazin
with Nicola Mestrino, 1748-1789, though there is some possibility of confusion
of the works of the two.   See also Anonymous, It. 1019.

1.   Sei Divertimenti / Per Violino Solo / Del Sig:r Nicoletto Sguazin   It. 392
     detto Mestre /   23x32.5cm. 10 st.
                                                                    WM: 33.
                                                                    Hand NNN. Brown.

F major

I.

E flat major

II.

B flat major

III.

E flat major

IV.

F minor

V.

A major

VI.

SIGHICELLI, GIUSEPPE, 1737-1826

Member of a family of violinists in Modena, he was chapel master for the house of Este in that city.

D major

1. Suonata / A Violino e Basso / Del Sig:ʳ Giuseppe / Sighicelli /

<u>It. 393</u>
score.
23.5x32cm. 10 st.
WM: 24.
Hand NN. Brown.

E flat major

2.   Suonata / A Violino e Basso / Del Sig.[r] Giuseppe / Sighicelli /

It. 394
score.
22.5x32cm. 10 st.
WM: 82.
Hand NN. Brown.

E major

3.   Suonata / A Violino e Basso / Del Sig:[r] Giuseppe / Sighicelli /

It. 395
score.
23x32cm. 10 st.
WM: 24.
Hand NN. Brown.

F major

4.   Suonata / A Violino e Basso / Del Sig:[r] Giuseppe / Sighicelli /

It. 396
score.
23x32cm. 10 st.
WM: 82.
Hand NN. Brown.

B flat major

5.   Suonata / a Violino e Basso / Del Signor Sighicelli /

It. 397
score.
23x32.5cm. 10 st.
WM: 82.
Hand NN. Brown.

STADE, FRANZ, fl. 1770

A violinist associated with the court chapel at Cassel intermittently from 1760 to 1764.   He was later active in Paris, Strassburg and Vienna.   Two sets of violin sonatas were published in Paris (ca. 1775-80) and two sets of variations in Vienna.

D major

1.   Sonata à Violino, e Basso / Del / Sig:[r] Francesco Stad /

It. 398
score.
23x32cm. 10 st.
WM: 29.
Hand A. Brown.

E major

2. Sonata a Violino, e Basso / Del / Sig:^r Francesco Stad /

It. 399
score.
23x32.5cm. 10 st.
WM: 29.
Hand A. Brown.

A major

3. Sonata a Violino, e Basso / Del / Sig.^r Francesco Stad /

It. 400
score.
23.5x32cm. 10 st.
WM: 29.
Hand A. Brown.

STAMITZ, JOHANN, 1717-1757

Violinist-composer best known for his work as concert master and director of chamber music in the court at Mannheim. He was appointed there in 1741. He spent a year in Paris, from September 1754 to September 1755, where much of his music was performed and published. He is credited with some 75 symphonies as well as concertos and music for chamber ensembles.

E flat major

1. Sonata à Violino, e Basso del Sig:^r Stamz /   It. 401

score.
23x32.5cm. 10 st.
WM: 3.
Hand A. Brown.

Listed by Riemann in __Mannheimer Kammermusik des 18.__
__Jahrhunderts__ as __Sonate op. 6 III__ (DTB, v. 16).

STERKEL, JOHANN FRANZ XAVER, 1750-1817

German musician, priest and keyboard virtuoso, he was born in Würzburg. In
1778 he was associated with the chapel of the Elector of Mainz at Aschaffen-
burg, and shortly thereafter traveled in Italy. An opera of his, __Farnace,__ was
produced in Naples. He composed much instrumental and vocal music, for
which a complete listing is given in Augustin Scharnagl's __Johann Franz Xaver__
__Sterkel, ein Beitrag zur Musikgeschichte Mainfrankens__ (Wurzburg, 1943).

1. No: VI / Suonate / A Due Violini e Basso / Del Sig:^r / Sterkel /   It. 402
    Basso /   v 1 & 2, bass.
                                                                 23x32.5cm. 10 st.
                          F major   WM: 43 & 47.
                                                                 Hand OOO. Brown.
    Triò I.

Listed by Riemann in __Mannheimer Kammermusik des 18.__
__Jahrhunderts__ as __Trio op. 6__ (DTB, v. 16).

B flat major

Trið II.

A major

Trið III.

Listed by Riemann in <u>Mannheimer Kammermusik des 18.</u>
<u>Jahrhunderts</u> as <u>Trio op. 6</u> (DTB, v. 16)

E flat major

Trið IV.

G major

Trið V.

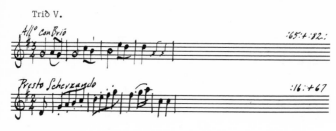

D major

Trið VI.

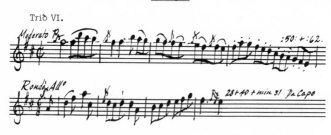

STRATICO, MICHELE, 1721?-1782?

Member of a noble family of Zara (now Zadar, Yugoslavia) Michele Stratico seems, like Albinoni, to have been an amateur violinist-composer rather than a professional musician. He is referred to in contemporary sources as a pupil of Tartini, and may well have studied with the latter during his years as a student of law at the University of Padua, 1737-1745. Scattered references indicate that his later places of residence were in or near Padua. Six of his sonatas were published in London by Peter Welcker, about 1763. The only known copy of this edition is in the University of California Music Library. Eitner's brief list of manuscript sources can be enlarged by the 156 sonatas, 14 duos, 35 trios, 15 sinfonie a 4, and 63 concertos of the Berkeley collection. In addition, there are scores of six trio sonatas by Stratico among the anonymous manuscripts at Cappella Antoniana in Padua; 16 sonatas, six quartets and a duo, as well as three volumes of treatises at the Marciana library in Venice; and two sonatas at the Library of Congress in Washington. A thematic catalog in the civic library at Ancona lists incipits for 59 sonatas, six published sonatas, 28 concertos and two duos.

<u>C major</u>

1.   Sonata a Violino e Basso / Del / Sig:^r Michiel Straticò /   It. 403

score.
23x30cm. 10 st.
WM: 19A.
Hand A. Brown.

Allegro is an extended version of that of Stratico Sonata It.409.

2.   Sonata a Violino e Basso / Del / Sig:^r Michiel Straticò /   It. 404

score.
23x30.5cm. 8 st.
WM: 63A.
Hand A. Brown.

Largo has the same thematic material as that of Stratico Concerto It.691 and the Andante of Stratico Sonata It.550.   The first
six measures, and 15 measures after the double bar are identical,
except that in Stratico Sonata It.550 the material has been transposed to B flat major.

3.   Sonata a Violino e Basso / Del / Sig^r Michel Straticò /   It. 405

score.
21.5x30cm. 8 st.
WM: 64.
Hand A. Brown.

4.   Sonata à Violino, e Basso / Del / Sig.^r Michele Stratico /

It. 406
score.
23x32.5cm. 10 st.
WM: 3.
Hand A^2. Black.

5.   Sonata a Violino e Basso / Del / Sig:^r Michiel Straticò /

It. 407
score.
22x30cm. 8 st.
WM: 63.
Hand A. Brown.

Affetuoso is the same as Andante of Stratico Concerto It.690
with additional trills. Allegro assai is the same as the solo
part of Allegro assai of Stratico Concerto It.679.

6.   No: 22 / Sonata a Violino e Basso / Del / Sig:^r Michiele
     Straticò /

It. 408
score.
22.5x30.5cm. 10 st.
WM: 50.
Hand A. Black.

7. Sonata a Violino e Basso / Del / Sig:ʳ Michiel Straticò /

It. 409
score.
21.5x29.5cm. 8 st.
WM: 64.
Hand A. Brown.

Allegro is a reduced version of that of Stratico Sonata It. 403.

8. Sonata a Violino e Basso / Del / Sig:ʳ Michele Stratico /

It. 410
score.
22x30cm. 8 st.
WM: 16.
Hand A. Black.

Published as no. 4 of Sei Sonate a Violino e Violoncello o
Clavicembalo ... Opera Prima. (London, Welcker, ca. 1763)

9. Sonata a Violino, e Basso / Del / Sig:ʳ Michele Stratico /

It. 411
score.
23x32cm. 10 st.
WM: 6.
Hand A. Brown.
(title in Hand B)

10. Sonata a Violino e Basso / Del / Sig:^r Michiel Straticò /

It. 412
score.
21.5x29.5cm. 8 st.
WM: 64.
Hand A. Brown.

Allegro has the same thematic material as that of Stratico Concerto It. 679.

11. Sonata a Violino, e Basso / Del / Sig:^r Michele Stratico /

It. 413
score.
23x29.5cm. 10 st.
WM: 65.
Hand A. Brown.

12. No: 10 / Sonata a Violino e Basso / Del / Sig:^r Michiele Straticò /

It. 414
score.
23x32cm. 10 st.
WM: 73.
Hand A. Black.

13. Sonata a Violino, e Basso / Del / Sig.ʳ Michele Straticò /

It. 415
score.
22x30cm. 10 st.
WM: unclear.
Hand A. Brown.

14. Sonata a Violino e Basso / Del / Sig.ʳ Michel Straticò /

It. 416
score.
22x30.5cm. 8 st.
WM: 50.
Hand A. Brown.

Adagio is a transposition of Largo (D major) of Stratico Sonata
It. 445.

15. Sonata a Violino e Basso / Del / Sigʳ Michiel Straticò /

It. 417
score.
23x30cm. 10 st.
WM: 19.
Hand A. Brown.

Andante is a transposition of Largo (E major) of Stratico Concerto
It. 688. Allegro 2 uses the same thematic material as that of
Stratico Sonata It. 421.

16. Sonata a Violino, e Basso / Del / Sig:ʳ Michele Stratico /

It. 418
score.
23.5x30cm. 10 st.
WM: 14.
Hand A. Black.

Published as no. 6 of <u>Sei Sonate a Violino e Violoncello o Clavi-cembalo</u> ... <u>Opera Prima.</u> (London, Welcker, ca. 1763)

17. No: 14 / Sonata a Violino è Basso / Del / Sig:ʳ Michiele Straticò/

It. 419
score.
22x31cm. 10 st.
WM: 64.
Hand A. Brown.

Embellished version of Largo: <u>It. 1007</u>:2.

18. Sonata a Violino, e Basso / Del / Sig:ʳ Michele Stratico /

It. 420
score.
23x32cm. 10 st.
WM: 84.
Hand A. Brown.

19. Sonata a Violino e Basso / Del / Sig:ʳ Michiel Straticò /

It. 421
score.
21.5x30.5cm. 8 st.
WM: 50.
Hand A. Brown.

Allegro 2 uses the same thematic material as that of Stratico
Sonata It. 417.

20. Sonata a Violino e Basso / Del / Sig:ʳ Michiel Straticò /

It. 422
score.
23x30cm. 10 st.
WM: 19.
Hand A. Brown.

Allegro assai is almost the same as the solo part of Allegro
assai of Stratico Concerto It. 677.

21. Sonata a Violino e Basso / Del / Sig:ʳ Michiel Straticò /

It. 423
score.
21.5x29cm. 8 st.
WM: 64.
Hand A. Brown.

22. No: 27 / Sonata a Violino e Basso / Del / Sigr. Michiele
    Straticò /

It. 424
score.
23x32cm. 10 st.
WM: 64.
Hand A. Brown.

23. Sonata a Violino, e Basso / Del / Sig.ʳ Michele Stratico /

It. 425
score.
23x32cm. 10 st.
WM: 6.
Hand A. Brown.

24. Sonata a Violino e Basso / Del / Sig:ʳ Michiele Straticò /

It. 426
score.
23x31.5cm. 10 st.
WM: 58.
Hand A. Brown.

D major

25. Sonata a Violino e Basso / Del / Sig:ʳ Michiel Straticò /

It. 427
score.
23x31cm. 10 st.
WM: 75.
Hand A. Brown.

The theme of Variazione is the same as that of Allegro of Stratico
Sonata It. 431 and Variazione of Stratico Sonata It. 450.

26. No: 30 / Sonata a Violino e Basso / Del / Sig:ʳ Michiel Straticò /

It. 428
score.
23x32cm. 10 st.
WM: 58.
Hand A. Brown.

Published with the third movement of It. 439 as no. 5 of Sei
Sonate a Violino e Violoncello o Clavicembalo ... Opera Prima.
(London, Welcker, ca. 1763)

27. Sonata a Violino, e Basso / Del / Sig:ʳ Michele Stratico /

It. 429
score.
22x31cm. 8 st.
WM: 16.
Hand A. Brown.

28. Sonata a Violino e Basso / Del / Sig^r Michiel Straticò /

It. 430
score.
23x30.5cm. 10 st.
WM: unclear.
Hand A. Brown.

Grave is the same as that of Stratico Sonata <u>It. 431</u> with an
altered bass.

29. Sonata a Violino e Basso / Del / Sig:^r Michiel Straticò /

It. 431
score.
23.5x30.5cm. 10 st.
WM: 19.
Hand A. Brown.

Grave is the same as that of Stratico Sonata <u>It. 430</u> with an
altered bass. The theme of Allegro 2 is the same as that of
Variazione of Stratico Sonata <u>It. 427</u> and Stratico Sonata <u>It. 450</u>.

30. Sonata / à Violino e Basso / Del / Sig:^r Michele Stratico /

It. 432
score.
23x31.5cm. 10 st.
WM: 4.
Hand A. Brown.

31. No: 23 / Sonata a Violino e Basso / Del / Sig.ʳ Michiele
    Straticò /

It. 433
score.
22.5x30cm. 10 st.
WM: unclear.
Hand A. Brown.

Embellished version of Largo andante: It. 1007:4.

32. Sonata a Violino e Basso / Del / Sig.ʳ Michiel Straticò /

It. 434
score.
22x30cm. 8 st.
WM: 63.
Hand A. Brown.

Andante is the same as Largo andante of Stratico Sonata It. 435
with fewer double stops. Allegro is the same as the solo part
of Allegro assai of Stratico Concerto It. 680.

33. Sonata a Violino e Basso / Del / Sig:ʳ Michiel Straticò /

It. 435
score.
23x29.5cm. 10 st.
WM: 19.
Hand A. Brown.

Largo andante is the same as Largo of Stratico Sonata It. 434
with additional double stops.

34. Sonata à Violino, e Basso / Del / Sig.ʳ Michele Straticò /

It. 436
score.
23x32.5cm. 10 st.
WM: 68.
Hand A². Black.

35. No: 31 / Sonata a Violino e Basso / Del / Sig:ʳ Michiel
     Straticò /

It. 437
score.
23x31.5cm. 10 st.
WM: 58.
Hand A. Brown.

36. Sonata a Violino e Basso / Del / Sig:ʳ Michiel Straticò /

It. 438
score.
23x30.5cm. 10 st.
WM: 58.
Hand A. Brown.

Largo andante is the same as Largo of Stratico Concerto It. 685.
Allegro is the same as the solo part of Allegro of Stratico Concerto It. 680.

37. Sonata a Violino e Basso / Del / Sig.^r Michel Straticò /

It. 439
score.
20x28.5cm. 8 st.
WM: 16.
Hand A. Brown.

Variazione published as the third movement of no. 5 of <u>Sei
Sonate a Violino e Violoncello o Clavicembalo</u> ... <u>Opera
Prima.</u> (London, Welcker, ca. 1763)

38. Sonata à Violino, e Basso / Del / Sig:^r Michele Straticò /

It. 440
score.
22.5x31cm. 10 st.
WM: 31.
Hand A. Brown.

39. Sonata à Violino, e Basso / Del / Sig.^r Michele Stratico /

It. 441
score.
23x32.5cm. 10 st.
WM: 3.
Hand A². Black.

40. Sonata a Violino, e Basso / Del / Sig:^r Michele Stratico /

It. 442
score.
22.5x30.5cm. 8 st.
WM: 16.
Hand A. Brown.

41. Sonata a Violino e Basso / Del / Sig:^r Michiel Straticò /

It. 443
score.
22x30.5cm. 8 st.
WM: 63.
Hand A. Brown.

Another copy. No: 16 / Sonata a Violino e Basso / Del / Sig:^r
Giuseppe Tartini / See It.715.

42. Sonata a Violino, e Basso / Del Sig:^r Michiele Stratico /

It. 444
score.
22.5x30cm. 10 st.
WM: 58.
Hand A. Black.

43. Sonata a Violino, e Basso / Del Sig:ʳ Michiele Stratico /

It. 445
score.
22.5x30cm. 10 st.
WM: 53.
Hand A. Black.

Largo is a transposition of Adagio (C major) of Stratico Sonata
It.416.

44. Sonata a Violino e Basso / Del / Sig:ʳ Michiel Straticò /

It. 446
score.
23x30cm. 10 st.
WM: 19A.
Hand A. Brown.

45. No: 21 / Sonata a Violino e Basso / Del / Sig:ʳ Michele
    Straticò /

It. 447
score.
23x31cm. 10 st.
WM: 50.
Hand A. Black.

46. Sonata à Violino, e Basso / Del / Sig:ʳ Michele Straticò /

It. 448
score.
22.5x31cm. 10 st.
WM: 31.
Hand A. Brown.

47. Sonata a Violino e Basso / Del / Sig:ʳ Michiel Straticò /

It. 449
score.
22.5x30.5cm. 10 st.
WM: 50.
Hand A. Brown.

48. Sonata a Violino e Basso / Del / Sig.ʳ Michiel Straticò /

It. 450
score.
23x29cm. 10 st.
WM: 19A.
Hand A. Brown.

Grave is the same as that of Stratico Sonata It. 451. The theme
of Variazione is the same as that of Variazione of Stratico Sonata
It. 427 and Allegro of Stratico Sonata It. 431.

49. Due sonate a Violino, e Basso / Del Sig:^r / Michiele Straticò /   It. 451
                                                                          score.

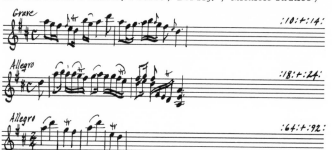
                                                                          25.5x36cm. 10 st.
                                                                          WM: 66.
                                                                          Hand B[2]. Black.

Grave is the same as that of Stratico Sonata It. 450.
For Sonata 2, see It. 503.

50. Sonata a Violino e Basso / Del / Sig:^r Michiel Straticò /   It. 452
                                                                          score.
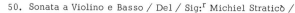

                                                                          21.5x29.5cm. 8 st.
                                                                          WM: 63.
                                                                          Hand A. Brown.

51. No: 8 / Sonata a Violino e Basso / Del / Sig:^r Michiele   It. 453
    Stratico /   score.

                                                                          23x32cm. 10 st.
                                                                          WM: 15.
                                                                          Hand A. Brown.

52. Sonata a Violino e Basso / Del / Sig:ʳ Michiel Straticò /

It. 454
score.
22.5x31.5cm. 10 st.
WM: 75.
Hand A. Brown.

53. No: 13 / Sonata a Violino e Basso / Del / Sig:ʳ Michiele
     Straticò /

It. 455
score.
23.5x31.5cm. 8 st.
WM: 19.
Hand A. Brown.

54. Sonata a Violino, e Basso / Del / Sig:ʳ Michele Stratico /

It. 456
score.
23x32cm. 10 st.
WM: 84.
Hand A. Brown.
(title in Hand B)

55. Sonata a Violino e Basso / Del / Sig:ʳ Michel Straticô /

It. 457
score.
21.5x29.5cm. 8 st.
WM: 64.
Hand A. Brown.

56. Sonata a Violino, e Basso / Del / Sigʳ Michele Stratico /

It. 458
score.
23x32cm. 10 st.
WM: 84.
Hand A. Brown.
(title in Hand B)

D minor

57. Sonata a Violino e Basso / Del / Sig:ʳ Michiel Straticô /

It. 459
score.
22.5x31cm. 8 st.
WM: 63A.
Hand A. Brown.

Allegro is the same as the solo part of Allegro of Stratico Concerto It. 683. Presto is the same as that of Stratico Sonata
It. 460, with minor differences in the bass.

58. Sonata a Violino e Basso / Del / Sig.^r Michiel Straticò /

It. 460
score.
21.5x29.5cm. 8 st.
WM: 64.
Hand A. Brown.

Larghetto is a transposed and reduced version of Larghetto (E
minor) of Stratico Sonata It. 471 and Stratico Sonata It. 472.
Presto is the same as that of Stratico Sonata It. 459, with
minor differences in the bass.

59. No: 28 / Sonata à Violino e Basso / Del / Sig:^r Michiele
Straticò /

It. 461
score.
22x30.5cm. 10 st.
WM: 12.
Hand A. Brown.

60. Sonata a Violino e Basso / Del / Sig:^r Michiel Straticò /

It. 462
score.
23x30cm. 10 st.
WM: 19.
Hand A. Black.

E flat major

61. Sonata / à Violino e Basso / Del / Sig.ʳ Michele Stratico /

It. 463
score.
22.5x31.5cm. 10 st.
WM: 15.
Hand A. Black.

E major

62. Sonata a Violino [e] Basso / Del / Sig:ʳ Michel Straticò /

It. 464
score.
22.5x30.5cm. 8 st.
WM: 50.
Hand A. Brown.

63. Sonata a Violino e Basso / Del / Sig:ʳ Michiel Straticò /

It. 465
score.
22.5x31cm. 10 st.
WM: 75.
Hand A. Brown.

Grave is the same as that of Stratico Sonata It. 466, with minor
differences. Variazione is the same as Cantabile of Stratico
Sonata It. 466.

64. Sonata a Violino, e Basso / Del Sig:ʳ Michiele Stratico /

It. 466
score.
22.5x30cm. 10 st.
WM: unclear.
Hand A. Black.

Grave is the same as that of Stratico Sonata It. 465, with minor
differences. Cantabile is the same as Variazione of Stratico
Sonata It. 465.

E minor

65. Sonata a Violino, e Basso / Del / Sig:ʳ Michele Stratico /

It. 467
score.
23.5x30cm. 10 st.
WM: 14.
Hand A. Brown.

66. Sonata a Violino, e Basso / Del / Sig.ʳ Michele Stratico /

It. 468
score.
23x32.5cm. 10 st.
WM: 67.
Hand A. Brown.

Another copy. Sonata / a Violino, e Basso / Del / Sig:ʳ
Michele Stratico /

Allegro is a more elaborate version of the thematic material.
Non Presto has 4 variations.

It. 469
score.
22.5x32cm. 10 st.
WM: 4.
Hand A. Brown.

67. No: 33 / Sonata a Violino e Basso / Del / Sig:ʳ Michiele
Straticò /

It. 470
score. .
23.5x32cm. 10 st.
WM: 58.
Hand A. Brown.

68. Sonata a Violino e Basso / Del / Sig:ʳ Michiel Straticò /

It. 471
score.
22x30.5cm. 8 st.
WM: 63A.
Hand A. Brown.

Larghetto is the same as that of Stratico Sonata It. 472 and a
transposed and extended version of Larghetto (D minor) of
Stratico Sonata It. 460. Presto has same thematic material as
Presto (G major) of Stratico Sonata It. 511.

69. Sonata a Violino e Basso / Del / Sig:ʳ Michiel Straticò /

It. 472
score.
21.5x29.5cm. 8 st.
WM: 63A.
Hand A. Brown.

Larghetto is the same as that of Stratico Sonata It. 471; and
a transposed and extended version of Larghetto (D minor) of
Stratico Sonata It. 460.

F major

70. No: 32 / Sonata a Violino e Basso / Del / Sig:ʳ Michiele
    Straticò /

It. 473
score.
23x32cm. 10 st.
WM: 58.
Hand A. Brown.

Embellished version of Largo: It. 1003:8.

71. Sonata a Violino, e Basso / Del / Sig.ʳ Michele Stratico /

It. 474
score.
23x32cm. 10 st.
WM: 3.
Hand A. Brown.

72. Sonata / a Violino e Basso / Del / Sig:ʳ Michele Stratico /

It. 475
score.
22.5x32cm. 10 st.
WM: 4.
Hand A. Brown.

All movements are the same as those of Stratico Sonata It. 486,
but with differences in figuration.

73. Sonata a Violino e Basso / Del / Sig:ͬ Michiel Straticò /   It. 476

score. .
22x30cm. 8 st.
WM: 63.
Hand A. Brown.

Allegro assai has same thematic material as Allegrò 2 of
Stratico Sonata It. 483.

74. Sonata a Violino e Basso / Del / Sig:ͬ Michel Straticò /   It. 477

score.
20.5x28.5cm. 8 st.
WM: 16.
Hand A. Brown.

75. Sonata a Violino, e Basso / Del / Sig.ͬ Michele Stratico /   It. 478

score.
23x32cm. 10 st.
WM: 6.
Hand A. Brown.

76. Sonata a Violino e Basso / Del / Sig.^r Michel Straticò /

It. 479
score.
21.5x29.5cm. 8 st.
WM: 64.
Hand A. Brown.

77. No: 34 / Sonata a Violino e Basso / Del / Sig:^r Michiele
    Straticò /

It. 480
score.
23x31cm. 10 st.
WM: 50.
Hand A. Brown.

78. Sonata a Violino e Basso / Del / Sig:^r Michiel Straticò /

It. 481
score.
23x30cm. 10 st.
WM: 19A.
Hand A. Brown.

Allegro assai is the same as that of Stratico Sonata It.482.

79. Sonata a Violino e Basso / Del / Sig:^r Michel Straticò /

It. 482
score.
23x30.5cm. 10 st.
WM: 53.
Hand A. Brown.

Allegro assai is the same as that of Stratico Sonata It. 481.

80. Sonata a Violino e Basso / Del / Sig:^r Michiel Straticò /

It. 483
score.
21.5x29.5cm. 8 st.
WM: 63.
Hand A. Brown.

Allegro 2 has same thematic material as Allegro assai of
Stratico Sonata It. 476.

81. Sonata à Violino, e Basso / Del / Sig.^r Michele Straticò /

It. 484
score.
22.5x31cm. 10 st.
WM: 31.
Hand A. Brown.

82. Sonata a Violino, e Basso / Del / Sig.^r Michele Stratico /

It. 485
score.
23x32.5cm. 10 st.
WM: 3.
Hand A² . Black.

83. Sonata a Violino, e Basso / Del / Sig:^r Michele Stratico /

It. 486
score.
23x32cm. 10 st.
WM: 5.
Hand A.   Brown.

All movements are the same as those of Stratico Sonata It. 475,
but with minor differences in figuration.

84. No: 3 / Sonata a Violino e Basso / Del / Sig:^r Michiele Stratico /

It. 487
score.
23.5x31cm. 8 st.
WM: 64.
Hand A.   Brown.

G major

85. No: 1 / Sonata a Violino, e Basso / Del / Sig:ʳ Michiele Stratico /

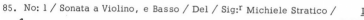

It. 488

score.
23.5x31.5cm. 8 st.
WM: 64.
Hand A. Brown.

86. Sonata a Violino, e Basso / Del Sig.ʳ Michele Stratico /

It. 489

score.
23x31.5cm. 10 st.
WM: 84.
Hand A. Black.

87. Sonata à Violino e Basso / Del / Sig:ʳ Michele Stratico /

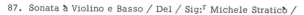

It. 490

score.
22.5x31.5cm. 10 st.
WM: 31.
Hand A. Brown.

88. Sonata a Violino e Basso / Del / Sig:ʳ Michiel Stratico /

It. 491
score.
23x29.5cm. 10 st.
WM: unclear.
Hand A. Black.

89. No: 18 / Sonata a Violino e Basso / Del / Sig:ʳ Michiele
      Straticò /

It. 492
score.
23x31cm. 10 st.
WM: 50.
Hand A. Black.

90. Sonata à Violino, e Basso / Del / Sig.ʳ Michele Stratico /

It. 493
score.
23x32.5cm. 10 st.
WM: 3.
Hand A². Black.

91. Sonata à Violino, e Basso / Del / Sig.ʳ Michele Straticò /

It. 494
score.
23x31.5cm. 10 st.
WM: 31.
Hand A. Brown.

92. Sonata a Violino, e Basso / Del Sig.ʳ Michele Stratico /

It. 495
score.
22x31.5cm. 10 st.
WM: 84.
Hand A. Black.

Published as no. 2 of Sei Sonate a Violino e Violoncello o
Clavicembalo ... Opera Prima. (London, Welcker, ca. 1763)

93. Sonata a Violino, e Basso / Del / Sig.ʳ Michele Stratico /

It. 496
score.
23x32.5cm. 10 st.
WM: 3.
Hand A². Black.

94. Sonata a Violino, e Basso / Del / Sig:ʳ Michele Stratico /

It. 497
score.
23x31.5cm. 10 st.
WM: 3.
Hand A. Black.

95. Sonata a Violino, e Basso / Del / Sig:ʳ Michele Stratico /

It. 498
score.
23x32cm. 10 st.
WM: 69.
Hand A. Brown.

96. No: 9 / Sonata a Violino e Basso / Del / Sig:ʳ Michiele
    Stratico /

It. 499
score.
22x30.5cm. 8 st.
WM: 77.
Hand A. Black.

97. Sonata a Violino, e Basso / Del / Sig:ʳ Michele Stratico /

:18:+:20:

It. 500
score.
22x30.5cm. 8 st.
WM: 16.
Hand A. Black.

:24:+:26:

:60:+:76:

98. No: 6 / Sonata a Violino e Basso / Del / Sig:ʳ Michiele Straticò /

:8:+:8:

It. 501
score.
23x32cm. 10 st.
WM: 73.
Hand A. Black.

:16:+:21:

:48:+:68:

99. Sonata a Violino e Basso / Del / Sig:ʳ Michiel Straticò /

:12:+:12:

It. 502
score.
22x30.5cm. 8 st.
WM: 63.
Hand A. Brown.

:76:+:116:

:56:+:76:

Grave is the same as that of Stratico Concerto It. 678, with
minor differences. Allegro is the same as the solo part of
Stratico Concerto It. 685, with additional double stops.

100. Sonata a Violino e Basso / Del / Sig^r Michiel Straticò /

It. 503
score.
22x30.5cm. 8 st.
WM: 63A.
Hand A. Brown.

Another copy. See It. 451.

101. No: 17 / Sonata a Violino e Basso / Del / Sig:^r Michiele
Straticò /

It. 504
score.
22x31cm. 10 st.
WM: 50.
Hand A. Black.

102. Sonata a Violino e Basso / Del / Sig:^r Michiel Straticò /

It. 505
score.
21.5x29.5cm. 8 st.
WM: 63A.
Hand A. Black.

103. Sonata a Violino e Basso / Del / Sig:^r Michel Straticò /

It. 506
score.
23x30.5cm. 10 st.
WM: unclear.
Hand A. Brown.

Allegro is the same as that of Stratico Sonata It.510.

104. Sonata a Violino, e Basso / Del Sig:^r Michiele Straticò /

It. 507
score.
23x31cm. 10 st.
WM: 12.
Hand A. Black.

105. Sonata a Violino e Basso / Del / Sig^r Michiel Straticò /

It. 508
score.
22.5x30.5cm. 10 st.
WM: unclear.
Hand A. Brown.

106. No: 4 / Sonata a Violino e Basso / Del / Sig:ʳ Michiele
    Stratico /

It. 509
score.
23x31cm. 8 st.
WM: unclear.
Hand A. Black.

107. Sonata a Violino, e Basso / Del Sig:ʳ Michiele Stratico /

It. 510
score.
23x30.5cm. 10 st.
WM: unclear.
Hand A. Black.

Allegro is the same as that of Stratico Sonata It.506.

108. Sonata a Violino e Basso / Del / Sig:ʳ Michel Straticò /

It. 511
score.
21.5x29.5cm. 8 st.
WM: 64.
Hand A. Brown.

Largo andante is the same as Largo of Stratico Sonata It.512.
Presto has the same thematic material as that of Stratico
Sonata It.471.

109. Sonata a Violino e Basso / Del / Sig:^r Michiel Straticò /

It. 512

score.
22x30cm. 8 st.
WM: 63A.
Hand A. Brown.

Largo is the same as Largo andante of Stratico Sonata It.511.

110. Sonata a Violino, e Basso / Del / Sig:^r Michele Stratico /

It. 513

score.
22x30cm. 10 st.
WM: 14.
Hand A. Brown.
(title in Hand B)

111. Sonata a Violino, e Basso / Del Sig:^r Michiele Stratico /

It. 514

score.
23x30cm. 10 st.
WM: 53.
Hand A. Black.

112. Sonata a Violino, e Basso / Del / Sig:^r Michele Stratico /

It. 515
score.
23x32cm. 10 st.
WM: 84.
Hand A. Brown.
(title in Hand B)

113. No: 29 / Sonata a Violino e Basso / Del / Sig:^r Michiele
     Straticò /

It. 516
score.
23x32cm. 10 st.
WM: 58.
Hand A. Brown.

Embellished version of Cantabile: It. 1003:7.

114. No: 12 / Sonata à Violino e Basso / Del / Sig.^r Michiele
     Straticò /

It. 517
score.
23.5x31.5cm. 8 st.
WM: 19A.
Hand A. Black.

115. Sonata a Violino e Basso / Del / Sig.^r Michiel Straticò /

It. 518
score.
22.5x30.5cm. 10 st.
WM: 50.
Hand A. Brown.

116. Sonata a Violino e Basso / Del / Sig.^r Michiel Straticò /

It. 519
score.
20.5x28.5cm. 8 st.
WM: unclear.
Hand A. Brown.

G minor

117. Sonata à Violino, e Basso / Del / Sig.^r Michele Straticò /

It. 520
score.
23x32cm. 10 st.
WM: 5.
Hand A². Brown.

118. Sonata a Violino e Basso / Del / Sig.ʳ Michiel Straticò /

It. 521
score.
22.5x29.5cm. 8 st.
WM: 63A.
Hand A. Brown.

119. Sonata a Violino, e Basso / Del Sig:ʳ Michiele Stratico /

It. 522
score.
23x30cm. 10 st.
WM: unclear.
Hand A. Brown.

A major

120. No: 24 / Sonata a Violino e Basso / Del / Sig:ʳ Michiele
Straticò /

It. 523
score.
23.5x31.5cm. 10 st.
WM: 67.
Hand A. Brown.

Another copy. No: 24 / Sonata a Violino e Basso / Del / Sig:ʳ
Michiele Straticò /

It. 524
score.
22.5x31.5cm. 10 st.
WM: 15.
Hand A. Brown.

121. No: 11 / Sonata a Violino e Basso / Del / Sig:ʳ Michele
Straticò /

It. 525
score.
22.5x31cm. 10 st.
WM: 64.
Hand A. Brown.

122. Sonata a Violino, e Basso / Del / Sig:ʳ Michele Straticò /

It. 526
score.
22.5x31.5cm. 10 st.
WM: 31.
Hand A. Brown.

123. No: 25 / Sonata a Violino e Basso / Del / Sig:ʳ Michiele
Straticò /

It. 527
score.
23.5x31.5cm. 8 st.
WM: 58.
Hand A. Brown.

Another copy, No: 25 / Sonata a Violino e Basso / Del / Sig:ʳ
Michiele Straticò /

It. 528
score.
23.5x31.5cm. 8 st.
WM: 67.
Hand A. Brown.

124. Sonata a Violino e Basso / Del / Sig:ʳ Michiel Straticỏ /

It. 529
score.
22x30.5cm. 8 st.
WM: 63.
Hand A. Brown.

Cantabile is the same as that of Stratico Sonata It.530.

125. Sonata a Violino e Basso / Del / Sig.ʳ Michiel Straticỏ /

It. 530
score.
22.5x31cm. 10 st.
WM: unclear.
Hand A. Brown.

Cantabile is the same as that of Stratico Sonata It.529.

126. Sonata a Violino, e Basso / Del / Sig:ʳ Michele Stratico /

It. 531
score.
22.5x29.5cm. 10 st.
WM: 14.
Hand A. Brown.

127. Sonata a Violino, e Basso / Del / Sig:ʳ Michele Stratico /

It. 532
score.
23x32.5cm. 10 st.
WM: 6.
Hand A. Brown.

128. Sonata a Violino e Basso / Del / Sig.ʳ Michel Straticò /

It. 533
score.
20.5x28.5cm. 8 st.
WM: 16.
Hand A. Brown.

129. No: 19 / Sonata a Violino e Basso / Del / Sig:ʳ Michiele
     Straticò /

It. 534
score.
22x30.5cm. 10 st.
WM: 50.
Hand A. Brown.

130. Sonata a Violino, e Basso / Del / Sig:^r Michele Stratico /

It. 535
score.
23.5x32.5cm. 10 st.
WM: 3.
Hand A. Brown.

Largo is the same as Grave of Stratico Sonata It.536. Non
presto has the same thematic material as Allegro of Stratico
Sonata It.536.

131. Sonata a Violino e Basso / Del / Sig:^r Michel Straticò /

It. 536
score.
22.5x30.5cm. 8 st.
WM: 50.
Hand A. Brown.

Grave is the same as Largo of Stratico Sonata It.535. Allegro 2
has the same thematic material as Non presto of Stratico Sonata
It.535.

132. Sonata a Violino e Basso / Del / Sig^r Michiel Straticò /

It. 537
score.
22.5x31cm. 10 st.
WM: 63.
Hand A. Brown.

Allegro assai is the same as the solo part of Allegro assai of
Stratico Concerto It.688.

133. No: 2 / Sonata a Violino, e Basso / Del / Sig:ʳ Michiele
     Stratico /

It. 538
score.
23.5x31cm. 8 st.
WM: unclear.
Hand A. Brown.

Embellished version of Largo: It. 1007:8, 1.

134. Sonata a Violino, e Basso / Del / Sig.ʳ Michele Stratico /

It. 539
score.
22x29.5cm. 10 st.
WM: 14 & 65.
Hand A. Brown.

135. Sonata à Violino, e Basso / Del / Sig.ʳ Michele Stratico /

It. 540
score.
23x32cm. 10 st.
WM: 68.
Hand A². Black.

136. Sonata a Violino, e Basso / Del Sig:ʳ Michiele Stratico /

It. 541
score.
22.5x31cm. 10 st.
WM: 69.
Hand A. Black.

137. No: 20 / Sonata a Violino e Basso / Del / Sig:ʳ Michiele
    Straticò /

It. 542
score.
23x31cm. 10 st.
WM: unclear.
Hand A. Brown.

138. Sonata / à Violino, e Basso / Del / Sig:ʳ Michele Stratico /

It. 543
score.
22.5x32cm. 10 st.
WM: 4.
Hand A. Black.

A minor

139. Sonata a Violino e Basso / Del / Sig:ʳ Michel Straticò /

It. 544
score.
21.5x29cm. 8 st.
WM: 64.
Hand A. Brown.

Largo is a transposition of Largo (B minor) of Stratico Concerto
It. 681. Allegro assai is the same as the solo part of Allegro
assai of Stratico Concerto It. 691.

140. Sonata à Violino, e Basso / Del / Sig.ʳ Michele Stratico /

It. 545
score.
23x32.5cm. 10 st.
WM: 3.
Hand A². Black.

141. No: 16 / Sonata a Violino e Basso / Del / Sig:ʳ Michiele
     Straticò /

It. 546
score.
23x32cm. 8 st.
WM: 19A.
Hand A. Brown.

142. Sonata à Violino, e Basso / Del / Sig:^r Michele Straticò /

It. 547
score.
22.5x31cm. 10 st.
WM: 56.
Hand A. Brown.

143. No: 7 / Sonata a Violino e Basso / Del / Sig:^r Michele
      Straticò /

It. 548
score.
23.5x31.5cm. 10 st.
WM: unclear.
Hand A. Black.

144. Sonata a Violino e Basso / Del Sig:^r Michele Stratico /

It. 549
score.
22.5x30cm. 10 st.
WM: unclear.
Hand A. Black.

B flat major

145. Sonata a Violino e Basso / Del / Sig:^r Michiel Straticò /

It. 550
score.
21.5x28.5cm. 8 st.
WM: unclear.
Hand A. Brown.

Andante is a transposition of Largo (C major) of Stratico Concerto It. 691, with added double stops. It has the same thematic material as Largo (C major) of Stratico Sonata It. 404.
The first six measures, and fifteen measures after the double
bar are identical except for transposition. Allegro assai is the
same as the solo part of Allegro of Stratico Concerto It. 692.
Presto is the same as the solo part of Allegro assai of Stratico
Concerto It. 692.

146. Sonata a Violino e Basso / Del / Sig:^r Michiel Straticò /

It. 551
score.
22x30cm. 8 st.
WM: 63.
Hand A. Black.

Grave has eight measures the same as those of Grave of
Stratico Sonata It. 552. Allegro assai is the same as Allegro
of Stratico Sonata It. 552.

147. Sonata a Violino e Basso / Del / Sig:ʳ Michel Straticò /

It. 552
score.
21.5x30cm. 8 st.
WM: 64.
Hand A. Brown.

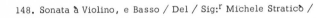

Grave has eight measures the same as those of Grave of
Stratico Sonata It. 551. Allegro is the same as Allegro assai
of Stratico Sonata It. 551.

148. Sonata à Violino, e Basso / Del / Sig:ʳ Michele Straticò /

It. 553
score.
22.5x31cm. 10st.
WM: 31.
Hand A. Brown.

149. Sonata à Violino, e Basso / Del / Sig.ʳ Michele Stratico /

It. 554
score.
23x32cm. 10 st.
WM: 68.
Hand A². Black.

150. Sonata à Violino, e Basso / Del / Sig.^r Michele Stratico /   It. 555

score.
23x33cm. 10 st.
WM: 3.
Hand A². Black.

151. Sonata a Violino, e Basso / Del / Sig.^r Michele Stratico /   It. 556

score.
22x29cm. 10 st.
WM: 14.
Hand A. Brown.

Published as no.1 of <u>Sei Sonate a Violino e Violoncello o Clavi-</u>
<u>cembalo</u> ... <u>Opera Prima.</u> (London, Welcker, ca. 1763)

152. No: 26 / Sonata a Violino e Basso / Del / Sig.^r Michiele   It. 557
Straticò /

score.
23x31.5cm. 10 st.
WM: 58.
Hand A. Brown.

Embellished version of Andante: <u>It. 1009</u>:3.

153. No: 15 / Sonata a Violino e Basso / Del / Sig:^r Michiele
    Straticò /

It. 558
score.
23.5x31.5cm. 8 st.
WM: 19.
Hand A. Black.

Embellished version of Affetuoso: It. 990:3.

B minor

154. No: 5 / Sonata a Violino e Basso / Del / Sig:^r Michiele
    Straticò /

It. 559
score.
23x31.5cm. 8 st.
WM: 71.
Hand A. Black.

Embellished version of Largo: It. 1003:2.

155. Sonata a Violino, e Basso / Del / Sig:^r Michele Stratico /

It. 560
score.
23x32cm. 10 st.
WM: 3.
Hand A. Brown.

156. Sonata a Violino e Basso / Del / Sig.^r Michel Straticò /

It. 561
score.
21.5x30cm. 8 st.
WM: 64.
Hand A. Brown.

Duets

C major

1. Divertimento da Camera a Due Violini Obbligati / Del Sig:^r
    Michele Straticò / Violino Primo /

It. 562
v 1 & 2.
22.5x31cm. 10 st.
WM: 31.
Hand A. Brown.

2. Divertimento da Camera a Due Violini Obbligati / Del Sig:^r
    Michele Straticò / Violino Primo /

It. 563
v 1 & 2.
22.5x31.5cm. 10 st.
WM: 31.
Hand A. Brown.

D major

3.   Divertimento da Camera a Due Violini Obbligati / Del Sig.[r]
     Michele Straticò / Violino Primo /

It. 564
v 1 & 2.
22.5x30.5cm. 10 st.
WM: 31.
Hand A.   Brown.

4.   Divertimento da Camera a Due Violini Obbligati / Del / Sig:[r]
     Michele Straticò / Violino Primo /

It. 565
v 1 & 2.
22.5x31cm. 10 st.
WM: 31.
Hand A.   Brown.

E minor

5.   Divertimento da Camera a Due Violini Obbligati / Del / Sig:[r]
     Michele Straticò / Violino Primo /

It. 566
v 1 & 2.
22.5x31cm. 10 st.
WM: 31.
Hand A.   Brown.

F major

6. Divertimento da Camera a Due Violini Obbligati / Del Sig:[r]
    Michele Straticò / Violino Primo /

It. 567
v 1 & 2.
22.5x31cm. 10 st.
WM: 31.
Hand A. Brown.

G major

7. Divertimento da Camera a Due Violini Obbligati / Del / Sig:[r]
    Michele Straticò / Violino Primo /

It. 568
v 1 & 2.
22.5x30.5cm.10 st.
WM: 31.
Hand A. Brown.

A major

8. Divertimento da Camera a Due Violini Obbligati / Del / Sig:[r]
    Michele Straticò / Violino Primo /

It. 569
v 1 & 2.
22.5x30.5cm.10 st.
WM: 31.
Hand A. Brown.

A minor

9. Divertimento da Camera a Due Violini Obbligati / Del Sig:[r]
    Michele Straticò / Violino Primo /

It. 570
v 1 & 2.
23x31cm. 10 st.
WM: 31.
Hand A. Brown.

B flat major

10. Divertimento da Camera a Due Violini Obbligati / Del / Sig:[r]
    Michele Straticò / Violino Primo /

It. 571
v 1 & 2.
22.5x31cm. 10 st.
WM: 31.
Hand A. Brown.

E flat major

11. Violino Primo / Duetto / Del Sig.[r] Michele Stratico /

It. 572
v 1 & 2.
23x32cm. 10 st.
WM: 51.
Hand A. Brown.

G major

12. Violino Primo / Duetto / Del Sig.^r Michele Stratico /

It. 573
v 1 & 2.
23x32cm. 10 st.
WM: 51.
Hand A. Brown.

E flat major

13. Sonata a Duè Violini / Del / Sig.^r Michele Stratico / Violino Primo /

It. 574
v 1 & 2.
22x30.5cm. 10 st.
WM: 4.
Hand A. Brown.

G major

14. Sonata à Due Violini / Del / Sig.^r Michele Stratico / Violino Primo /

It. 575
v 1 & 2.
22x30.5cm. 10 st.
WM: 4.
Hand A. Brown.

Trios

C major

1. Violino Primo / Sonata da Camera à Tre / Del Sig.^r Michele
    Stratico /

It. 576
v 1 & 2, bass.
23x31.5cm. 10 st.
WM: 15.
Hand A. Brown.

2. Sonata a Tre / Del Sig:^r Michele Stratico / Basso /

It. 577
v 1 & 2, bass.
23x32cm. 10 st.
WM: 16.
Hand A. Brown.

D major

3. Sonata a Tre / Del Sig:^r Michele Stratico / Basso /

It. 578
v 1 & 2, bass.
23x31.5cm. 10 st.
WM: 16.
Hand A. Brown.

Another copy. Andante [and] Allegro [and Andante and Allegro
of It. 581]

It. 579
[v 1]
23.5x31.5cm. 10 st.
WM: 16.
Hand A. Brown.

E flat major

4.   Violino Primo / Sonata da Camera à Trè / Del Sig.[r] Michele
     Stratico /

It. 580
v 1 & 2, bass.
22.5x31.5cm. 10st.
WM: 15, 4, 59.
Hand A.   Brown.

E major

5.   Sonata a Trè / Del Sig:[r] Michele Stratico / Basso /

It. 581
v 1 & 2, bass.
23x32.5cm. 10 st.
WM: 16.
Hand A.   Brown.

Another copy.   Andante [and] Allegro.   See It. 579.

F major

6.   Sonata a Trè / Del Sig:[r] Michele Stratico / Basso /

It. 582
v 1 & 2, bass.
23x32cm. 10 st.
WM: 16.
Hand A.   Brown.

G major

7. Sonata da Camera / a Trê / Del Sig.ʳ Michele Stratico / Basso /

It. 583
v 1 & 2, bass.
23x33cm. 10 st.
WM: 3A.
Hand A. Brown.

8. Sonata a Trê / Del Sig:ʳ Michele Stratico / Basso /

It. 584
v 1 & 2, bass.
23x32cm. 10 st.
WM: 16.
Hand A. Brown.

A major

9. Sonata a Trê / Del Sig:ʳ Michele Stratico / Basso /

It. 585
v 1 & 2, bass.
23x32cm. 10 st.
WM: 16.
Hand A. Brown.

10. Sonata da Camera / a Trê / Del Sig.^{r} Michele Stratico / Basso /

It. 586
v 1 & 2, bass.
22.5x32.5cm. 10 st.
WM: 3A.
Hand A. Brown.

A minor

11. Violino Primo / Sonata da Camera à Trê / Del Sig.^{r} Michele
Stratico /

It. 587
v 1 & 2, bass.
23x32cm. 10 st.
WM: 15 & 59.
Hand A. Brown.

B flat major

12. Sonata da Camera / à Trê / Del Sig.^{r} Michele Stratico / Basso /

It. 588
v 1 & 2, bass.
23.5x31.5cm. 10 st.
WM: 9 & 3A.
Hand A. Brown.

C major

13. Trio / Del Sig.^r Michel Stratico / Basso /

It. 589
v 1 & 2, bass.
22.5x30cm. 10 st.
WM: 63A.
Hand A. Brown.

D major

14. Trio / Del Sig.^r Michel Stratico / Basso /

It. 590
v 1 & 2, bass.
22.5x29.5cm. 10 st.
WM: 63A.
Hand A. Brown.

15. Trio / Del Sig^r Michiel Stratico / Basso /

It. 591
v 1 & 2, bass.
22x30cm. 10 st.
WM: 63A.
Hand A. Brown.

F major

16. Trio / Del Sig.^r Michel Stratico / Basso /

It. 592
v 1 & 2, bass.
22x31cm. 10 st.
WM: 69 & 63A.
Hand A. Brown.

G major

17. Trio / Del Sig.^r Michiel Stratico / Basso /

It. 593
v 1 & 2, bass.
22x31cm. 10 st.
WM: 69.
Hand A. Brown.

18. Trio / Del Sig.^r Michel Stratico / Basso /

It. 594
v 1 & 2, bass.
22x30cm. 10 st.
WM: 63A.
Hand A. Brown.

A major

19. Trio / Del Sig.^r Michel Stratico / Basso /

It. 595
v 1 & 2, bass.
22x31cm. 10 st.
WM: 69.
Hand A. Brown.

B flat major

20. Trio / Del Sig.^r Michel Stratico / Basso /

It. 596
v 1 & 2, bass.
22x31cm. 10 st.
WM: 69.
Hand A. Brown.

C major

21. Sinfonia a 3 / Del / Sig:^r Michiele Straticò / Violino P:mo /

It. 597
v 1 & 2, bass.
22x31cm. 8 st.
WM: 77A.
Hand A. Black.

22. Sinfonia / Del / Sig:^r Michiel Straticò /

It. 598
v 1 & 2 [bass]
22.5x30cm. 8 st.
WM: 63A.
Hand A. Black.

D major

23. Sinfonia a 3 / Del / Sig:^r Michiele Straticò / Violino Primo /

It. 599
v 1 & 2, bass.
22x30cm. 8 st.
WM: 77.
Hand A. Black.

24. Sinfonia a tre / Del / Sig:^r Michiel Straticò / Basso /

It. 600
v 1 & 2, bass.
21.5x30cm. 8 st.
WM: 63.
Hand A. Black.

25. Sinfonia a tre / Del / Sig:ʳ Michiel Straticò / Basso /

It. 601
v 1 & 2, bass.
21.5x29.5cm. 8 st.
WM: 63.
Hand A. Black.

D minor

26. Sinfonia a tre / Del / Sigʳ Michiel Straticò / Basso /

It. 602
v 1 & 2, bass.
22.5x30cm. 8 st.
WM: 63.
Hand A. Black.

27. Sinfonia a tre / Del / Sig:ʳ Michiel Straticò / Basso /

It. 603
v 1 & 2, bass.
22x31cm. 8 st.
WM: 63 & 63A.
Hand A. Black.

F major

28. Sinfonia a tre / Del / Sig:^r Michiel Straticò /

It. 604
v 1 & 2 [bass]
22x30.5cm. 8 st.
WM: 63.
Hand A. Black.

F minor

29. Sinfonia a tre / Del / Sig:^r Michiel Straticò / Basso /

It. 605
v 1 & 2, bass.
22x30.5cm. 8 st.
WM: 63.
Hand A. Black.

G major

30. Sinfonia a 3 / Del / Sig:^r Michiel Straticò / Basso /

It. 606
v 1 & 2, bass.
22x31cm. 8 st.
WM: 63 & 63A.
Hand A. Black.

31. Sinfonia a 3 / Del / Sig:ʳ Michiele Straticò / Violino P:mo /   It. 607
v 1 & 2, bass.
22.5x31cm. 8 st.
WM: 77.
Hand A. Black.

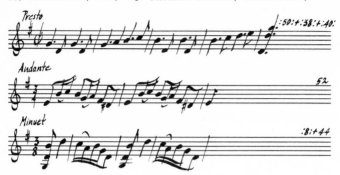

32. Sinfonia a tre / Del / Sig:ʳ Michiel Straticò /   It. 608
v 1 & 2 [bass]
21.5x30.5cm. 8 st.
WM: 63A.
Hand A. Black.

33. Sinfonia a 3 / Del / Sig:ʳ Michiele Straticò / Violino P:mo /   It. 609
v 1 & 2, bass.
23x31cm. 8 st.
WM: 77.
Hand A. Black.

A major

34. Sinfonia á 3 / Del / Sig:ʳ Michiele Straticò / Violino P:mo /

It. 610
v 1 & 2, bass.
22.5x31cm. 8 st.
WM: 77.
Hand A. Black.

B flat major

35. Sinfonia a 3 / Del / Sig:ʳ Michiele Straticò / Violino P:mo /

It. 611
v 1 & 2, bass.
22.5x31cm. 8 st.
WM: 77.
Hand A. Black.

Quartets

C major

1. Sinfonia a 4 / Del / Sig:ʳ Michiele Stratico / Violino P:mo /

It. 612
v 1 & 2, vla, bass.
23.5x32cm. 8 st.
WM: 19 & 19A.
Hand A. Black.

2.   Sinfonia a 3 / Del / Sig:ʳ Michiel Straticò /

It. 613
v 1 & 2, vla, bass.
22x30.5cm. 8 st.
WM: 63.
Hand A. Black.

Andante is the same as that of Stratico Sinfonia It. 614.

3.   Sinfonia a 4 / Del Sig:ʳ Michele Straticò / Basso /

It. 614
v 1 & 2, vla, bass.
23.5x32.5cm. 8 st.
WM: 64.
Hand A. Brown.

Andante is the same as that of Stratico Sinfonia It. 613.

C minor

4.   Sinfonia a 3 / Del / Sig:ʳ Michiel Straticò /

It. 615
v 1 & 2, vla, bass.
22x30.5cm. 8 st.
WM: 63.
Hand A. Black.

D major

5. Sinfonia / Del / Sig:^{r} Michiel Straticò / Basso /

It. 616
v 1 & 2, vla, bass.
22x31cm. 8 st.
WM: 63.
Hand A. Black.

Minuet is the same as Non presto of Stratico Sinfonia It. 618.

6. Sinfonia a 4 / Del / Sig:^{r} Michiele Straticò / Violino P:mo /

It. 617
v 1 & 2, vla, bass.
23.5x32cm. 8 st.
WM: 19.
Hand A. Black.

7. Sinfonia a 4 / Del / Sig:^{r} Michiele Straticò / Violino Primo /

It. 618
v 1 & 2, vla, bass.
23x33cm. 8 st.
WM: 15.
Hand A. Brown.

Non presto is the same as Minuet of Stratico Sinfonia It. 616.

D minor

8. Sinfonia a 4 / Del / Sig:ʳ Michiele Straticò / Violino Primo /

It. 619
v 1 & 2, vla, bass.
23.5x31cm. 10 st.
WM: unclear.
Hand A. Brown.

F major

9. Sinfonia a 4 / Del / Sig:ʳ Michiele Straticò / Violino Primo /

It. 620
v 1 & 2, vla, bass.
23x31.5cm. 10 st.
WM: 50.
Hand A. Brown.

10. Sinfonia a 4 / Del / Sig:ʳ Michiele Straticò / Basso /

It. 621
v 1 & 2, vla, bass.
23x31cm. 10 st.
WM: 50.
Hand A. Brown.

11. Sinfonia a 4 / Del / Sig:ʳ Michele Straticò / Basso /

It. 622
v 1 & 2, vla, bass.
23x32cm. 8 st.
WM: 64.
Hand A. Brown.

G major

12. Sinfonia a 4 / Del / Sig:ʳ Michele Straticò / Violino P:mo /

It. 623
v 1 & 2, vla, bass.
24x32cm. 8 st.
WM: 19.
Hand A. Black.

13. Sinfonia a 4 / Del / Sig:ʳ Michele Straticò / Basso /

It. 624
v 1 & 2 obl, vla,
bass.
23x32cm. 8 st.
WM: 50.
Hand A. Brown.

A major

14. Sinfonia a 4 / Del / Sig:ʳ Michiele Straticò / Basso /

It. 625
v 1 & 2, vla, bass.
23.5x31.5cm. 8 st.
WM: 19.
Hand A. Black.

B flat major

15. Sinfonia a 4 / Del / Sig:ʳ Michiele Straticò / Vioilno P:mo /

It. 626
v 1 & 2, vla, bass.
21.5x29.5cm. 8 st.
WM: 77.
Hand A. Brown.

Concertos

D major

1. Concerto a due Violini Obbligati / Del / Sig:ʳ Michel Straticò /
    Violino Primo Obbligato /

It. 627
v 1, 2 & 3 obl, v 1
rip (2 copies) v 2
rip, vla, vlc obl,
bass rip.
22x31.5cm. 10 st.
WM: 83 & 53.
Hand A. Brown.

2.   Concerto a due Violini Obbligati / Del / Sig:^r Michel Straticò /
    Violino Primo Obblig.^{to} /

It. 628
v 1 & 2 obl, v 1 & 2
rip, vla obl, vla
rip, vlc obl, bass
rip.
23x30.5cm. 10 st.
WM: unclear & 53.
Hand A. Brown.

Concerti a 5

C major

3.   No: 11 / Violino Principale / Concerto / Del / Sig:^r Michiele
    Straticò /

It. 629
vp, v 1 & 2 obl,
vla, vlc obl.
23x31cm. 10 st.
WM: 64.
Hand A. Brown.

4.   Violino Principale / Concerto / Del Sig.^r Michele Stratico /

It. 630
vp, v 1 & 2 obl,
vla, vlc obl.
23x30.5cm. 10 st.
WM: 64 & 79.
Hand A. Brown.

5.   Violino Principale / Concerto / Del / Sig:ʳ Michiel Straticò /

It. 631
vp, v 1 & 2 obl,
vla, vlc obl,
bass.
22x30.5cm. 8 st.
WM: 63 & 69.
Hand A. Black.
(bass in Hand B)

6.   Violino Principale / Concerto / Del Sig:ʳ Michele Stratico /

It. 632
vp, v 1 & 2 obl,
vla, vlc obl.
22.5x31cm. 8 st.
WM: 69.
Hand A. Brown.

7.   Violino Principale / Concerto / Sopra un Aria Francese di
     Michiel Straticò /

It. 633
vp, v 1 & 2 obl,
vla obl, vlc obl.
22.5x30.5cm. 8 st.
WM: 63 & 19.
Hand A. Brown.

Another copy. Violino Principale / Concerto alla Francese /
Del Sigʳ: / Michele Stratico /

It. 634
vp, v 1 & 2 obl,
[vla] [bass]
23x32cm. 10 st.
WM: 16.
Hand A. Brown.

8.   Violino Principale / Concerto / Del Sig.[r] Michele Stratico /

It. 635
vp, v 1 & 2 obl,
vla, vlc obl.
22x31cm. 10 st.
WM: 6.
Hand A. Black.

9.   No: 16 / Violino Principale / Concerto / Del / Sig:[r] Michele
     Straticò /

It. 636
vp, v 1 & 2 obl,
vla, vlc obl.
21.5x30cm. 8 st.
WM: 1.
Hand A. Brown.

10. Violino Principale / Concerto / Del Sig:[r] Michele Stratico /

It. 637
vp, v 1 & 2 obl,
vla, vlc obl.
22.5x30.5cm. 10 st.
WM: 64 & 50.
Hand A. Brown.

Embellished version of Largo: It. 1009:1.

11. Violino Principale / Concerto / Del Sig[r]: Michele Stratico /

Embellished version of Largo: It. 1005:20.

It. 638
vp, v 1 & 2 obl,
vla, vlc obl.
22.5x31cm. 10 st.
WM: 4.
Hand A. Brown.

D major

12. No: 10 / Violino Principale / Concerto / Del / Sig:[r] Michiele
Straticò /

It. 639
vp, v 1 & 2 obl,
vla, vlc obl.
22x30cm. 8 st.
WM: 77A.
Hand A. Brown.

13. Violino Principale / Concerto / Del / Sig[r]: Michiel Straticò /

It. 640
vp, v 1 & 2 obl,
vla, vlc obl.
22x29.5cm. 8 st.
WM: 16.
Hand A. Brown.

Non presto is the same as Allegro of Stratico Concerto It. 641.
Allegro assai is an extended version of that of Stratico Concerto
It. 641.

14. No: 6 / Violino Principale / Concerto / Del / Sig:ᵣ Michiele
     Straticò /

Allegro is the same as Non presto of Stratico Concerto It.640.
Allegro assai is a shorter version of that of Stratico Concerto
It.640.

It. 641
vp, v 1 & 2 obl,
[vla] vlc obl.
23x31.5cm. 10 st.
WM: unclear.
Hand A. Black.

15. Violino Principale / Concerto / Del Sig.ᵣ Michele Stratico /

It. 642
vp, v 1 & 2 obl,
vlc, vlc obl.
22.5x31.5cm. 10 st.
WM: 69 & 6.
Hand A. Black.

Another copy. Violino Principale / Concerto / Del Sig:ᵣ Michele
Stratico /

It. 643
vp, v 1 & 2 obl,
vla, vlc obl.
22x31cm. 10 st.
WM: 4.
Hand A. Brown.

16. Violino Principale / Concerto / Del Sig:ᵣ Michele Straticò /

It. 644
vp, v 1 & 2 obl,
vla, vlc obl.
22.5x32cm. 10 &
8 st.
WM: 16 & 58.
Hand A. Brown.

17. Violino Principale / Concerto / Del Sig:ʳ Michele Stratico /

It. 645
vp, v 1 & 2 obl,
vla, vlc obl.
22.5x31cm. 8 &
10 st.
WM: 50 & 29.
Hand A. Brown.

18. No: 2 / Violino Principale / Concerto / Del Sig:ʳ Michiele
    Straticồ /

It. 646
vp, v 1 & 2 obl,
vla, vlc obl,
violon.
22x30.5cm. 8 &
10 st.
WM: 62.
Hand A. Brown.
(violon in Hand B)

19. Violino Principale / Concerto / Del Sig:ʳ Michele Stratico /

It. 647
vp, v 1 & 2 obl,
vla, vlc obl.
22x31cm. 8, 10
& 12 st.
WM: 50 & 29.
Hand A. Brown.

20. Violino Principale / Concerto / Del Sig:ʳ Michele Stratico /

It. 648
vp, v 1 & 2 obl,
vla, vlc obl.
22.5x30.5cm. 10 st.
WM: 63 & 64.
Hand A. Brown.

21. Violino Principale / Concerto / Del Sig:ʳ Michele Stratico /

It. 649
vp, v 1 & 2 obl
[vla] vlc obl.
22.5x29.5cm. 10 st.
WM: 65.
Hand A. Brown.

22. Violino Principale / Concerto / Del Sig:ʳ Michele Straticò /

It. 650
vp, v 1 & 2 obl,
vla, vlc obl.
22x31cm. 10 & 8 st.
WM: 6 & unclear.
Hand A. Brown.

23. Violino Principale / Concerto / Del Sig.^r Michele Stratico /

It. 651

vp, v 1 & 2 obl,
vla, vlc obl.
22.5x31cm. 10 st.
WM: 69.
Hand A. Brown.

Embellished version of Grave: It.1005:28.

24. Violino Principale / Concerto / Del Sig:^r Michele Stratico /

It. 652

vp, v 1 & 2 obl,
vla, vlc obl.
23x30.5cm. 10 st.
WM: 64 & 63A.
Hand A. Brown.

25. No: 13 / Violino Principale / Concerto / Del Sig:^r Michiele
    Straticò /

It. 653

vp, v 1 & 2 obl,
vla, vlc obl.
23x30.5cm. 8 st.
WM: 19.
Hand A. Brown.

F major

26. Violino Principale / Concerto / Del / Sig:ʳ Michiel Straticò /

It. 654
vp, v 1 & 2 obl,
vla, vlc obl.
22x30.5cm. 8 st.
WM: 63.
Hand A. Brown.

Another copy. Concerto / Del / Sig:ʳ Giuseppe Tartini / 1768 /
See It. 900.

27. Violino Principale / Concerto / Del Sig:ʳ Michele Stratico /

It. 655
vp, v 1 & 2 obl,
vla, vlc obl.
22.5x31.5cm. 10 st.
WM: 16.
Hand A. Brown.

Embellished version of Andante: It. 1009:4 (fragment)

G major

28. Violino Principale / Concerto / Del / Sig:ʳ Michiel Straticò /

It. 656
vp, v 1 & 2 obl.
vla, bass.
21.5x29cm. 8 st.
WM: 64.
Hand A. Brown.

Embellished version of Andante: It. 1009:2.

29. Violino Principale / Concerto / Del Sig:ʳ Michele Stratico /

It. 657
vp, v 1 & 2 obl,
vla, vlc obl.
22.5x30.5cm. 10 st.
WM: 63A & 32.
Hand A. Brown.

30. Violino Principale / Concerto / Del Sig:ʳ Michele Stratico /

It. 658
vp, v 1 & 2 obl,
[vla] vlc obl.
22.5x30.5cm. 10 st.
WM: 69.
Hand A. Brown.

31. Violino Principale / Concerto / Del Sig.ʳ Michele Stratico /

It. 659
vp, v 1 & 2 obl,
vla, vlc obl.
22.5x31.5cm. 8 &
10 st.
WM: 16 & 4.
Hand A. Brown.

Another copy. No: 12 / Violino Principale / Concerto / Del /
Sig:ʳ Michiele Straticò /

It. 660
vp, v 1 & 2 obl,
vla, vlc obl.
23x31.5cm. 10 st.
WM: 64.
Hand A. Black.

32. Violino Principale / Concerto / Del Sig:^r Michele Stratico /

It. 661
vp, v 1 & 2 obl,
vla, vlc obl.
22.5x31cm. 8 &
10 st.
WM: 50 & unclear.
Hand A. Brown.

33. No: 3 / Violino Principale / Concerto / Del / Sig:^r Michiele
Straticò /

It. 662
vp, v 1 & 2 obl,
vla, vlc obl.
23x31cm. 8 st.
WM: 71.
Hand A. Black.

34. No: 8 / Violino Principale / Concerto / Del / Sig:^r Michiele
Straticò /

It. 663
vp, v 1 & 2 obl,
vla, vlc obl
[bass]
21.5x30cm. 8 st.
WM: 77A.
Hand A. Brown.
(bass in Hand B)

35. No: 4 / Violino Principale / Concerto / Del / Sig:ʳ Michiele
Straticò /

It. 664
vp, v 1 & 2 obl,
v 2, vla, vlc obl,
bass.
23.5x32cm. 8 st.
WM: 19 & 27A.
Hand A. Brown.
(v 2 & bass in
Hand B)

Embellished version of Grave: It. 1010:6.

36. Violino Principale / Concerto / Del Sig:ʳ Michele Stratico /

It. 665
vp, v 1 & 2 obl,
vla, vlc obl.
23x31cm. 10 st.
WM: 63A.
Hand A. Brown.

Embellished version of Largo: It. 1005:30.

37. No: 15 / Violino Principale / Concerto / Del / Sig:ʳ Michiele
Straticò /

It. 666
vp, v 1 & 2 obl,
vla, bass.
21.5x31cm. 10 &
8 st.
WM: 64 & 19A.
Hand A. Black.

Embellished version of Grave: It. 1005:14.

<u>G minor</u>

38. Violino Principale / Concerto / Del Sig.ʳ Michele Stratico /

It. 667
vp, v 1 & 2 obl,
vla, vlc obl.
22.5x31.5cm.
10 & 8 st.
WM: 6.
Hand A.   Black.

Embellished version of Grave: It. 1005:18.

<u>A major</u>

39. Violino Principale / Concerto / Del / Sig:ʳ Michiel Straticò /

It. 668
vp, v 1 & 2 obl,
vla obl, vlc obl.
22.5x31cm. 8 st.
WM: 50.
Hand A.   Brown.

40. Violino Principale / Concerto / Del Sig.ʳ Michele Stratico /

It. 669
vp, v 1 & 2 obl,
vla, vlc obl.
22x29cm. 10 st.
WM: 65.
Hand A.   Brown.
(parts in another
hand)

41. Violino Principale / Concerto / Del Sig:ʳ Michele Stratico /

It. 670
vp, v 1 & 2 obl,
vla, vlc obl.
22.5x30cm. 10 st.
WM: 64 & 29.
Hand A. Brown.

42. Violino Principale / Concerto / Del Sig.ʳ Michele Stratico /

It. 671
vp, v 1 & 2 obl,
vla, vlc obl.
23x31cm. 10 st.
WM: 69 & 16.
Hand A. Brown.

A minor

43. Violino Principale / Concerto / Del Sig.ʳ Michele Stratico /

It. 672
vp, v 1 & 2 obl,
vla, vlc obl.
22.5x31cm. 10 st.
WM: 4.
Hand A. Brown.

44. No: 5 / Violino Principale / Concerto / Del / Sig:ʳ Michiele
    Straticð /

It. 673
vp, v 1 & 2 obl,
vla, vlc obl.
22.5x31cm. 8 &
10 st.
WM: 71.
Hand A. Black.

B flat major

45. Violino Principale / Concerto / Del / Sig:ʳ Michiel Straticð /

It. 674
vp, v 1 & 2 obl,
vla, vlc obl,
bass.
22.5x31cm. 10 &
8 st.
WM: 63A.
Hand A. Black.
(bass in Hand B)

Allegro is the same as Allegro 2 of Tartini Concerto It. 942.

46. Violino Principale / Concerto / Del Sig.ʳ Michele Stratico /

It. 675
vp, v 1 & 2 obl,
vla, vlc obl.
22.5x31.5cm. 10 st.
WM: 68.
Hand A². Brown.

Concerti a 4

C major

47. No: 14 / Violino Principale / Concerto / Del Sig:^r Michiele
Straticò /

It. 676
vp, v 1 & 2 obl,
bass.
23x30.5cm. 8 st.
WM: 19.
Hand A. Black.

48. Violino Principale / Concerto / Del / Sig:^r Michiel Straticò /

It. 677
vp, v 1 & 2 obl,
bass.
22x30.5cm. 8 st.
WM: 63A.
Hand A. Brown.

Allegro assai has solo passages almost identical with Allegro
assai of Stratico Sonata It. 422.

49. Violino Principale / Concerto / Del Sig:^r Michiel Straticò /

It. 678
vp, v 1 & 2 obl,
bass.
22.5x31cm. 10 &
8 st.
WM: 64 & 50.
Hand A. Brown.

Grave is the same as that of Stratico Sonata It. 502, with minor
differences.

50. Violino Principale / Concerto / Del / Sig:^r Michiel Straticò /

It. 679
vp, v 1 & 2 obl,
bass.
22x30.5cm. 8 st.
WM: 63.
Hand A. Black.

Allegro has the same thematic material as that of Stratico
Sonata It. 412. Allegro assai has solo passages identical
with the Allegro assai of Stratico Sonata It. 407.

D major

51. Violino Principale / Concerto / Del / Sig:^r Michiel Straticò /

It. 680
vp, v 1 & 2 obl,
bass.
22x31cm. 8 st.
WM: 63A.
Hand A. Black.

Allegro has solo passages identical with Allegro of Stratico
Sonata It. 438. Allegro assai has solo passages identical with
Allegro of Stratico Sonata It. 434.

52. Violino Principale / Concerto / Del / Sig:^r Michiel Straticò /

It. 681
vp, v 1 & 2 obl,
bass.
22x30.5cm. 8 st.
WM: 63A.
Hand A. Brown.

Largo is a transposition of Largo (A minor) of Stratico Sonata
It. 544.

53. No: 9 / Violino Principale / Concerto / Del / Sig:ʳ Michiele
Straticò /

It. 682
vp, v 1 & 2 obl,
bass.
22x30cm. 8 st.
WM: 77.
Hand A. Brown.

E minor

54. Violino Principale / Concerto / Del / Sig:ʳ Michiel Straticò /

It. 683
vp, v 1 & 2 obl,
bass.
22x30.5cm. 8 st.
WM: 63.
Hand A. Brown.

Allegro has solo passages identical with Allegro of Stratico
Sonata It. 459.

G major

55. No: 1 / Violino Principale / Concerto / Del Sig:ʳ Michiele
Straticò /

It. 684
vp, v 1 & 2 obl,
bass.
23.5x31cm. 8 st.
WM: 64.
Hand A¹. Brown.

56. Violino Principale / Concerto / Del / Sig:ʳ Michiel Straticò /

It. 685
vp, v 1 & 2 obl,
bass.
22x30.5cm. 10 &
8 st.
WM: 63.
Hand A. Brown.

Allegro has solo passages identical with Allegro of Stratico
Sonata It.502. Largo is the same as Largo andante of Stratico
Sonata It.438.

57. Violino Principale / Concerto / Del Sig:ʳ Michele Stratico /

It. 686
vp, v 1 & 2 obl,
vlc obl.
21.5x30.5cm. 8 &
10 st.
WM: 14 & 29.
Hand A. Black.

A major

58. Violino Principale / Concerto / Del / Sig.ʳ Michiel Straticò /

It. 687
vp, v 1 & 2 obl,
bass.
22x31cm. 8 st.
WM: 63.
Hand A. Brown.

59. Violino Principale / Concerto / Del / Sig:^r Michiel Straticò /

It. 688
vp, v 1 & 2 obl,
bass.
22.5x30.5cm. 8 st.
WM: 63.
Hand A. Brown.

Allegro assai has solo passages identical with Allegro assai of
Stratico Sonata It. 537. Largo is a transposition of Andante (C
major) of Stratico Sonata It. 417.

60. No: 7 / Violino Principale / Concerto / Del / Sig:^r Michiele
Straticò /

It. 689
vp, v 1 & 2 obl
[bass]
23x30.5cm. 10 &
8 st.
WM: 27 & unclear.
Hand A. Black.

A minor

61. Violino Principale / Concerto / Del / Sig.^r Michiel Straticò /

It. 690
vp, v 1 & 2 obl,
bass.
22.5x30.5cm. 8 st.
WM: 64.
Hand A. Brown.

Andante is the same as Affetuoso of Stratico Sonata It. 407,
with fewer trills.

62. Violino Principale / Concerto / Del / Sig:ʳ Michiel Straticò /

It. 691
vp, v 1 & 2 obl,
bass.
22x30.5cm. 8 st.
WM: 63A.
Hand A. Brown.

Allegro has solo passages identical with Allegro assai of
Stratico Sonata It. 544. Largo is a transposition of Andante
(B flat major) of Stratico Sonata It. 550. It has the same
thematic material as Largo of Stratico Sonata It. 404. The first
six measures, and fifteen measures after the double bar are
identical.

B flat major

63. Violino Principale / Concerto / Del / Sig:ʳ Michiel Straticò /

It. 692
vp, v 1 & 2 obl,
[bass]
22.5x31cm. 8 st.
WM: 63.
Hand A. Brown.

Allegro has solo passages identical with Allegro assai of
Stratico Sonata It. 550. Allegro assai has solo passages
identical with Presto of Stratico Sonata It. 550.

The figure of Tartini provides the keystone upon which the structure of the present collection depends. This observation can be made not merely for the abundance of his own work represented (110 sonatas or sonata movements, 106 concertos, 15 trios and three quartets) but because of the fact that the repertoire is dominated by the works of musicians who came under his direct influence. Thirteen of the violinist-composers in the Berkeley collection are listed among Tartini's pupils: Alberghi, Bini, Ferrari, Fracassini, Helendaal, Holzbogen, Manfredi, Morigi, Nardini, Nazari, Dall'Oglio, Stratico and Touchemoulin. Others, such as Barbella, Capuzzi, Mosel, Raimondi and Viotti, have a connection only slightly less direct. From 1721 to the end of his life, with the exception of two years in Prague, Tartini devoted himself to the musical life of Padua as solo violinist and "capo di concerto" at St. Anthony's, as a teacher and as a theorist. One of the most striking pieces of evidence of his teaching activity, in relation to the Berkeley collection, is the presence of a large number of embellished slow movements from his sonatas and concertos. Further, the collection contains a manuscript copy of the original Italian text of Tartini's treatise on embellishment, formerly known under the French title, Traité des Agrémens.

Recent bibliographical work on the Tartini sources has made it possible to dispense with thematic quotations for the sonatas and concertos. The sonatas are identified with the number assigned them in the thematic catalog given in Paul Brainard's Die Violinsonaten Giuseppe Tartinis (Diss. Göttingen, 1959); the concertos take their identifying symbol from Minos Dounias' Die Violinkonzerte Giuseppe Tartinis, Wolfenbüttel-Berlin, 1935.

Collections

1. Sonate da Camera à / Violino e Basso / Del Sig:ᵣ Giuseppe
   Tartini di Padova / Opera Seconda /

   Contents: B. D 13, B. G 18, B. A 17, B. h 6, B. a 10, B. C 12,
   B. g 11, B. D 14, B. B 9; B. F 8, B. e 8, B. G 19.

   Manuscript copy of op. 2, published Rome, Cleton, 1745. A
   copy of this edition is in the University of California Music
   Library.

   It. 693
   score.
   23x31.5cm. 10 st.
   WM: 41 & 30.
   Hand U. Brown.

2. Num:ʳᵒ Sei / Sonate per il Violino / Del Sig.ᵣ Giuseppe Tartini /

   Cover title.

   Contents: B. g 3, B. G 8, B. D 11, B. a 7, B. C 12, B. A 6.
   On page 1 in Hand F: Minueti del Sigior Igiacio Xaueri·Da
   Gorizia, 1778. On page 3: Allegro B. g 14 (4th movement);
   p. 32-33: Adagio B. A 15 (1st movement).

   It. 694
   score.
   22.5x30.5cm. 10 st.
   WM: 69 & 64.
   Hands P & F.
   Brown.

Sonatas

C major

1. No: 46 / Sonata a Violino e Basso / Del / Sig:^{r} Giuseppe
    Tartini /

    > Andante cantabile
    > Allegro assai
    > Presto

    B. C 1. Brainard gives one additional movement.
    Version with double stops.

    It. 695
    score.
    22x30cm. 8 st.
    WM: 71.
    Hand A. Black.

    Another copy. Sonata a Violino, e Basso / Del / Sig:^{r}
    Giuseppe Tartini /

    B. C 1.

    It. 696
    score.
    23x31cm. 10 st.
    WM: 53.
    Hand A. Brown.

2. Sonata a Violino e Basso / Del / Sig:^{r} Giuseppe Tartini /

    > Largo
    > Allegro
    > Allegro

    B. C 4. Brainard gives one additional movement.

    It. 697
    score.
    23x31.5cm. 10 st.
    WM: 12.
    Hand A. Brown.

    Another copy. Sinfonia a Violino Solo del Sig.^{r} Tartini. No: 4 /

    > Largo
    > Allegro
    > Adagio
    > Allegro

    B. C 4.
    Caption title.

    It. 698
    score.
    23.5x31.5cm. 10 st.
    WM: 70.
    Hand N^1. Brown.

3. Sonata a Violino, e Basso / Del / Sig:^{r} Giuseppe Tartini /

    > Andante
    > Allegro
    > Allegro assai

    B. C 5. Brainard gives one additional movement.

    It. 699
    score.
    22.5x31cm. 10 st.
    WM: 6.
    Hand A. Brown.

4. Sonata à Violino, e Basso del Sig.^r Giuseppe Tartini /   It. 700
                                                                                         score.
        Andante cantabile   23.5x32cm. 10 st.
        Allegro   WM: 36.
        Allegro   Hand A. Brown.
        Presto
        Menuetto

    B. C 6.
    Caption title.

5. Sonata à Violino, e Basso del Sig.^r Giuseppe Tartini /   It. 701
                                                                                         score.
        Grave   22x31cm. 10 st.
        Allegro   WM: 3A.
        Allegro   Hand A. Brown.

    B. C 8.
    Caption title.

6. No: 31 / Sonata a Violino e Basso / Del / Sig:^r Giuseppe   It. 702
    Tartini /   score.
                                                                                         23x31.5cm. 10 st.
        Adagio   WM: 64.
        Allegro   Hand A. Black.
        Allegro

    B. C 9.
    Embellished version of Adagio: It. 988:12, It. 994:14.

    Son: 6:^{ta}. In Collection no.1. It. 693.

        Largo andante
        Allegro
        Presto assai

    B. C 12.
    Embellished version of Largo andante: It. 989:2, It. 994:4.
    Published as no.6 of Opus II (Rome, Cleton, 1745)

    Another copy. [Sonata] 5. In Collection no. 2. It. 694.

    B. C 12.

7. Sonata a Violino e Basso del Sig:^{r} Giuseppe Tartini /   It. 703
                                                                       score.
        Largo   22.5x32cm. 10 st.
        Allegro   WM: 3A.
        Allegro   Hand A. Brown.

    B. C 13.
    Caption title.

                        C minor

8. Sonate a Violino, e Basso / Del / Sig:^{r} / Giuseppe Tartini /   It. 704
                                                                       score.
        Grave   22.5x32.5cm. 10 st.
        Allegro non presto   WM: 5.
        Allegro   Hand B. Black.

    B. c 1.
    Embellished version of Grave: It.988:26, It. 1012:2.

    Another copy. Suonata a Violino Solo, e Basso / Del Sig:^{r} It. 705
    Giuseppe Tartini / No: 18 /   score.
                                                                      23x31.5cm. 10 st.
    B. c 1.   WM: unclear.
    Caption title.   Hand N^2. Brown.
    Bass figured.   (title in Hand L)

9. Sonata a Violino e Basso / Del Sig:^{r} Giuseppe Tartini /   It. 706
                                                                      score.
        Allegro   22x30.5cm. 10 st.
        Allegro   WM: unclear.
                                                                      Hand A. Brown.
    B. c 4.

                        D major

10. No: 44 / Sonata / à Violino e Basso / Del / Sig:^{r} Giuseppe   It. 707
    Tartini /   score.
                                                                      22.5x30.5cm. 8 st.
        Andante cantabile   WM: unclear.
        Allegro   Hand A. Black.
        Giga
        Allegro

    B. D 1. Brainard gives two additional movements.
    Version with double stops.

11. Sonata a Violino, e Basso / Del / Sig:^r Giuseppe Tartini /   It. 708
                                                                         score.
        Larghetto   22x31cm. 10 st.
        Allegro   WM: 4.
        Allegro assai   Hand A. Brown.

    B. D 7.
    Embellished version of Larghetto: It. 1014:2.

12. No: 27 / Sonata à Violino, e Basso / Del Sig:^r Giuseppe   It. 709
    Tartini /   score.
                                                                         23x31.5cm. 10 st.
        Largo   WM: 64.
        Allegro   Hand N.   Brown.
        Allegro

    B. D 8.
    Caption title.
    Embellished version of Largo: It. 988:24.
    Published as no. 3 of Opus VI (Paris, LeClerc, ca. 1748)

13. Sonata à Violino, e Basso Del Sig.^r Giuseppe Tartini /   It. 710
                                                                         score.
        Andante   22.5x31.5cm. 10 st.
        Allegro   WM: 68.
        Allegro assai   Hand A. Brown.
        Cantabile
        Minuetto

    B. D 9.
    Caption title.
    Version with double stops.

14. No: 33 / Sonata a Violino e Basso / Del / Sig:^r Giuseppe   It. 711
    Tartini /   score.
                                                                         23x31.5cm. 10 st.
        Grave   WM: 64.
        Allegro   Hand A.   Black.
        Allegro

    B. D 10.
    Published as no. 6 of Opus VII (Paris, Maupetit, ca. 1750)

    Sonata 3:^za. In Collection no. 2. It. 694.

        Andante
        Allegro
        Allegro

    B. D 11.
    Published as no. 1 of Opus VII (Paris, Maupetit, ca. 1750)

Sonata Pma. In Collection no.1. It. 693.

    [Andante cantabile]
    Allegro
    Affettuoso
    Allegro assai

B. D 13.
Published as no.1 of Opus II (Rome, Cleton, 1745)

15. No: 41 / Sonata / a / Violino, e Basso / Del Sig:^{r} / Giuseppe   **It. 712**
    Tartini /   score.
                                              23.5x30cm. 10 st.
    Andante   WM: 14A.
    Allegro   Hand B^1. Brown.
    Allegro assai

B. D 14.
Version with double stops.
Published as no.8 of Opus II (Rome, Cleton, 1745)

Another copy. Sonata 8:^{va}. In Collection no.1. It. 693.

B. D 14.

16. Sonata a Violino, e Basso Del Sig.^{r} Giuseppe Tartini /   **It. 713**
                                              score.
    Largo   22.5x32cm. 10 st.
    Allegro   WM: 3A.
    Allegro assai   Hand A. Brown.

B. D 15.
Caption title.
Published as no.5 of Opus IV (Paris, Hue, 1747)

Sonata a Violino, e Basso / Del / Sig.^{r} Domenico dall'Oglio /
see It. 331.

B. D 17.

17. Suonata del Sig:^{r} Giuseppe Tartini /   **It. 714**
                                            score.
    Adagio   22.5x31cm. 10 st.
    Allegro   WM: 32 & unclear.
    Andante   Hand H^2. Brown.
    Allegro   (title in another
                                              hand)

B. D 19.
Caption title.

18. No: 16 / Sonata a Violino e Basso / Del / Sig:ʳ Giuseppe
Tartini /

    Largo
    Allegro
    ...

B. D 20.

It. 715
score.
23.5x31.5cm. 10 st.
WM: unclear.
Hand G. Black.
(title in Hand B)

Another copy. Sonata a Violino e Basso / Del / Sig:ʳ Michiel
Stratico / see It. 443

B. D 20.

Sonata a Violino e Basso / Del Sigʳ Domenico Ferrari /
see It. 163.

B. D 21.

19. Sonata a Violino, e Basso / Del / Sig:ʳ Giuseppe Tartini /

    Variazioni

B. D 22.

It. 716
score.
21.5x30cm. 8 st.
WM: 17.
Hand A. Brown.

D minor

20. No: 43 / Sonata / a / Violino e Basso / Del / Sig:ʳ Giuseppe
Tarini /

    Andante
    Allegro
    Allegro

B. d 1.
Version with double stops.

It. 717
score.
22.5x30.5cm. 8 st.
WM: 62.
Hand A. Brown.

Another copy. Sonata a Violino, e Basso / Del / Sig:ʳ Giuseppe
Tartini /

B. d 1.

It. 718
score.
23x30.5cm. 10 st.
WM: 53.
Hand A. Brown.

21. No: 15 / Sonata / à Violino, e Basso / Del Sig:ʳ Giuseppe
    Tartini /

    Largo
    Allegro
    Allegro

B. d 4.
Embellished version of Largo: It. 1012:6.
Published as no.3 of Opus II (Amsterdam, Le Cene, 1743)

It. 719
score.
23x31.5cm. 10 st.
WM: unclear.
Hand D. Brown.

Another copy. No: 15 / Sonata a / Violino, e Basso / Del Sig:ʳ
Giuseppe Tartini /

B. d 4.
Bass figured.

It. 720
score.
23.5x30.5cm. 10 st.
WM: 14A.
Hand B¹. Black.

22. Sonata a Violino, e Basso Del Sig:ʳ Giuseppe Tartini /

    Larghetto
    Allegro
    Presto
    Minuetto

B. d 5. Brainard gives one additional movement.
Caption title.

It. 721
score.
22.5x32.5cm. 10 st.
WM: 3A.
Hand A. Brown.

E major

23. Sonata a Violino e Basso / Del / Sigʳ Giuseppe Tartini /

    Andante cantabile
    Allegro
    Allegro assai
    Minuet

B. E 1. Brainard gives two additional movements.
Version with double stops.

It. 722
score.
22.5x30cm. 8 st.
WM: 58.
Hand A. Brown.

24. Sonata a Violino, e Basso / Del Sig.ʳ Giuseppe Tartini /

    Grave
    Allegro
    Allegro

B. E 3.
Caption title.
Published as no.1 of Opus IV (Paris, Hue, 1747)

It. 723
score.
22.5x32.5cm. 10 st.
WM: 3A.
Hand A. Brown.

25. No: 29 / Sonata / a Violino, e Basso / Del Sig:ʳ Giuseppe
 Tartini /

    Andante
    Allegro assai
    Allegro assai

It. 724
score.
23.5x30.5cm. 10 st.
WM: unclear.
Hand B¹. Black.

B. E 4.
Embellished version of Andante: It. 988:14.
Published as no. 4 of Opus VII (Paris, Maupetit, ca. 1750)

26. No: 3 / [Without title]

    Grave
    Allegro
    Allegro

It. 725
score.
23x32cm. 10 st.
WM: unclear.
Hand B¹. Black.

B. E 6.
Embellished version of Grave: It. 988:16, It. 994:10, It. 1013:1.
Fragment in another hand on last page.
Published as no. 6 of Opus II (Amsterdam, Le Cene, 1743)

E minor

27. Sonata a Violino e Basso / Del / Sig:ʳ Giuseppe Tartini /

    Andante cantabile
    Allegro cantabile
    Allegro

It. 726
score.
22x30cm. 8 st.
WM: 58.
Hand A. Black.

B. e 1. Brainard gives two additional movements.
Version with double stops.

Another copy. Sonata a Violino, e Basso / Del / Sigʳ Giuseppe
Tartini /

B. e 1.

It. 727
score.
23x30.5cm. 10 st.
WM: 53.
Hand A. Brown.

28. Sonata a Violino e Basso / Del / Sig:ʳ Giuseppe Tartini /

    Adagio
    Allegro
    Allegro

It. 728
score.
22.5x31cm. 10 st.
WM: 22.
Hand A. Brown.

B. e 5.

29. No: 6 / [Without title]   It. 729
                                                                 score.
            Grave   23.5x31.5cm. 10 st.
            Allegro   WM: unclear.
            Presto   Hand T. Brown.

     B. e 7.
     Embellished version of Grave: It.988:6, It.1014:3.
     Fragments in another hand on covers.
     Bass figured.
     Published as no.4 of Opus II (Amsterdam, Le Cene, 1743)

     Sonata 11:ma. In Collection no.1. It.693.

            Andante cantabile
            Allegro
            Allegro

     B. e 8.
     Published as no.11 of Opus II (Rome, Cleton, 1745)

                              F major

30. No: 47 / Sonata a Violino e Basso / Del / Sig:r Giuseppe   It. 730
     Tartini /   score.
                                                                 22x30cm. 8 st.
            Andante cantabile   WM: 71.
            Allegro assai   Hand A. Black.
            Allegro

     B. F 1. Brainard gives two additional movements.
     Version with double stops.

     Another copy. Sonata a Violino, e Basso / Del / Sig.r Giuseppe   It. 731
     Tartini /   score.
                                                                 23x30.5cm. 10 st.
            Andante cantabile   WM: unclear.
            Allegro   Hand A. Brown.
            Allegro

     B. F 1. Brainard gives two additional movements.

31. No: 13 / Sonata / a Violino, e Basso / Del Sig:r / Giuseppe   It. 732
     Tartini /   score.
                                                                 23x30cm. 10 st.
            Grave   WM: 14A.
            Allegro   Hand B1. Black.
            Allegro

     B. F 3.
     Embellished version of Grave: It.988:22, It.994:9, It.1013:3.
     Bass figured.

32. Sonata a Violino e Basso / Del / Sig:^r Giuseppe Tartini /   <u>It. 733</u>
                                                                        score.
    Adagio   23x31cm. 10 st.
    Allegro   WM: 58.
    Allegro assai   Hand A. Brown.

    B. F 6. Brainard gives one additional movement.
    Published as no. 5 of Opus IX (Paris, Le Clerc, ca. 1760)

33. No: 26 / Sonata / Del Sig^r: / Giuseppe Tartini / a Violino, e   <u>It. 734</u>
    Basso /   score.
                                                                        22.5x31cm. 10 st.
    Adagio   WM: 62.
    Allegro   Hand B². Black.
    Allegro

    B. F 7.
    Embellished version of Adagio: <u>It. 1014</u>:2.
    Published as no. 6 of Opus VII (Paris, Maupetit, ca. 1750)

    Sonata 10:^{ma}. In Collection no. 1. <u>It. 693</u>.

    Andante allegro
    Andante largo
    Allegro assai

    B. F 8.
    Embellished version of Andante largo: <u>It. 989</u>:4, <u>It. 994</u>:6.
    Published as no. 10 of Opus II (Rome, Cleton, 1745)

34. No: 5 / Sonata á Violino e Basso / Del Sig^r: Giuseppe Tartini /   <u>It. 735</u>
                                                                        score.
    Larghetto   23x31.5cm. 10 st.
    Allegro   WM: 72.
    Minuet   Hand E. Black.
                                                                        (title in another
    B. F 13.   hand)
    Bass figured.

                               <u>G major</u>

35. No: 48 / Sonata á Violino e Basso / Del / Sig:^r Giuseppe Tartini/ <u>It. 736</u>
                                                                        score.
    Andante sciolto   22x30cm. 8 st.
    Andante cantabile   WM: 71.
    Allegro   Hand A. Brown.

    B. G 1. Brainard gives two additional movements.

36. Sonata a Violino e Basso / Del / Sig:[r] Giuseppe Tartini /   It. 737
                                                                       score.
    Andante   21x31cm. 8 st
    Variazione   WM: 83.
                                                                       Hand A. Brown.
    B. G 2. Brainard gives four additional movements.
    Version with double stops.

37. Sonata a Violino e Basso del Sig:[r] Giuseppe Tartini /   It. 738
                                                                       score.
    Andante   22x30cm. 10 st.
    Variazione   WM: 63.
                                                                       Hand A. Brown.
    B. G 2. Brainard gives four additional movements.
    Version with double stops.

38. Sonata a Violino e Basso / Del / Sig:[r] Giuseppe Tartini /   It. 739
                                                                       score.
    Andante (B. G 5, movement 4)   22.5x30.5cm. 8 st.
    Allegro   WM: 58.
    Allegro   Hand A. Brown.
    Allegro (B. G 4, movement 4)

    B. G 3. Brainard gives one additional movement.
    Version with double stops.

39. Sonata a Violino e Basso / Del / Sig:[r] Giuseppe Tartini /   It. 740
                                                                       score.
    Andante cantabile   22.5x30.5cm. 8 st.
    Allegro assai   WM: unclear.
    Andante cantabile   Hand A. Brown.

    B. G 4. Brainard gives one additional movement.
    Version with double stops.
    Superscription, Andante cantabile: Sento spirarmi sul volto lieve
    fiato che lento s'aggiri, sono questi gli estremi sospiri del mio
    fido che more per me.

40. Sonata a Violino, e Basso / Del / Sig:[r] Giuseppe Tartini /   It. 741
                                                                       score.
    Largo   22x31cm. 10 st.
    Allegro   WM: 4.
    Allegro   Hand A. Brown.

    B. G 7.

41. No: 12 / Sonata / a / Violino e Basso / Del Sig^r: Giuseppe
    Tartini /

    Grave
    Allegro assai
    Presto

B. G 8.
Embellished version of Grave: It.988:8.
Bass figured.
Published as no.1 of Opus VI (Paris, Le Clerc, ca.1748)

It. 742
score.
23x31.5cm. 10 st.
WM: unclear.
Hand B^2. Black.

Another copy. [Sonata] No.2. In Collection no.2. It.694.

B. G 8.

42. No: 22 / Sonata a Viol:^{no} e Basso / Del Sig:^{r} / Giuseppe
    Tartini /

    Adagio
    Allegro
    Allegro assai

B. G 9.
Embellished version of Adagio: It.988:98, It.994:12.
Bass figured.
Published as no.3 of Opus VII (Paris, Maupetit, ca.1750)

It. 743
score.
23x30.5cm. 10 st.
WM: 14A.
Hand B^1. Black.

43. No: 9 / Sonata / à Violino solo, e Basso / del Sig^r: Giuseppe
    Tartini /

    Largo, mà andante
    Allegro
    Allegro assai

B. G 10.
Embellished version of Largo, mà andante: It.988:10.
Published as no.6 of Opus VI (Paris, Le Clerc, ca.1748)

It. 744
score.
23x31cm. 10 st.
WM: unclear.
Hand D. Brown.

44. No: 28 / Sonata à / Violino e Basso / Del Sig^r: Giuseppe
    Tartini /

    Largo
    Allegro
    Allegro

B. G 11. Brainard gives one additional movement.
Caption title.

It. 745
score.
22.5x30.5cm. 10 st.
WM: 77A.
Hand N. Brown.

45. Sonata a Violino e Basso / Del / Sig:ʳ Giuseppe Tartini /   It. 746
                                                                       score.
      Andante   21x29.5cm. 8 st.
      Allegro   WM: 63.
      Aria cantabile   (B. G 2, movement 3)   Hand A. Black.

    B. G 14. Brainard gives three additional movements.
    Superscription, Aria cantabile: Quanto mai felici siete innocenti
    pastorelle.

46. [Without title]   It. 747
                                                                       score.
      Allegro   23x32.5cm. 10 st.
      Minuetto   WM: 56.
      Adagio   (B. A 11, movement 2)   Hand A³. Brown.

    B. G 14. Brainard gives three additional movements.

47. Sonata a Violino e Basso / Del / Sig:ʳ Giuseppe Tartini /   It. 748
                                                                       score.
      Largo   23x32cm. 10 st.
      Allegro   WM: 12.
      Allegro   Hand A. Brown.

    B. G 15.

    Sonata 2ᵈᵃ. In Collection no.1. It.693.

      Andante
      Affetuoso
      Allegro assai

    B. G 18.
    Embellished version of Andante: It.989:6, It.991:3.
    Published as no.2 of Opus II (Rome, Cleton, 1745)

48. No: 39 / Sonata / A / Violino, e Basso / Del Sig:ʳ / Giuseppe   It. 749
    Tartini /   score.
                                                                       23x30.5cm. 10 st.
      Andante   WM: unclear.
      Allegro   Hand B¹. Black.
      Presto assai

    B. G 19.
    Embellished version of Andante: It.988:60, It.994:3, It.1003:4.
    Bass figured.
    Published as no.12 of Opus II (Rome, Cleton, 1745)

    Another copy. Sonata 12:ᵐᵃ. In Collection no.1. It.693.

    B. G 19.

49. Sonata a Violino e Basso / Del / Sig:^{r} Giuseppe Tartini /

It. 750
score.
23x32cm. 10 st.
WM: 12.
Hand A. Brown.

Grave
Allegro
Allegro

B. G 20.
Published as no. 2 of Opus IV (Paris, Hue, 1747)

50. No: 1 / Sonata à Violino e Basso /

It. 751
score.
23x31.5cm. 10 st.
WM: unclear.
Hand E. Black.

Largo andante
Allegro mà non presto
Aria, andante e cantabile

B. G 21. Brainard gives one additional movement.
Published as no. 4 of Opus V (Paris, Hue, ca. 1748)

51. Sonata a Violino e Basso / Del / Sig:^{r} Giuseppe Tartini /

It. 752
score.
22.5x31.5cm. 10 st.
WM: 12.
Hand A. Brown.

Grave
Allegro
Allegro

B. G 28.

52. Sonata a Violino e Basso / Del / Sig:^{r} Giuseppe Tartini /

It. 753
score.
22.5x31.5cm. 10 st.
WM: 84.
Hand A. Brown.

Adagio
Allegro
Allegro

B. G 29.

Another copy. Sonata à Violino, e Basso del Sig.^{r} Domenico
Dall' Oglio / see It. 340.

B. G 29.

53. Sonata a Violino, e Basso / Del / Sig:^{r} Giuseppe Tartini /

It. 754
score.
23x32.5cm. 12 st.
WM: unclear.
Hand A. Brown.

Adagio
Allegro
Allegro

B. G 30.

Another copy. No: 23 / Sonata / a Violino, e Basso / Del Sig:ʳ   It. 755
Giuseppe Tartini /   score.
                                                                        23x30cm. 10 st.
B. G 30.   WM: 14A.
                                                                        Hand B¹. Black.

G minor

54. No: 49 / Sonata a Violino e Basso / Del / Sig:ʳ Giuseppe   It. 756
    Tartini /   score.
                                                                        22.5x30.5cm. 8 st.
      Andante   WM: 71.
      Allegro   Hand A. Brown.
      Affettuoso
      Allegro assai

    B. g 1.
    Version with double stops.

    Another copy. Sonata a Violino, e Basso / Del / Sig:ʳ Giuseppe   It. 757
    Tartini /   score.
                                                                        23x30.5cm. 10 st.
    B. g 1.   WM: 53.
                                                                        Hand A. Brown.

55. Sonata a Violino e Basso / Del / Sig:ʳ Giuseppe Tartini /   It. 758
                                                                        score.
      Andante cantabile   21.5x29.5cm. 8 st.
      Allegro   WM: 63.
      Allegro non presto   Hand A. Black.
      Presto
      Allegro non presto

    B. g 2.

56. No: 35 / Sonata a Violino, e Basso / Del / Sig.ʳ Giuseppe   It. 759
    Tartini /   score.
                                                                        23x30.5cm. 10 st.
      Largo andante   WM: 27.
      Allegro   Hand B. Black.
      Giga

    B. g 3. Brainard gives one additional movement.
    Embellished version of Largo andante: It. 988:28, It. 990:4,
    It. 991:4, It. 1012:4.
    Published as no. 5 of Opus VII (Paris, Maupetit, ca. 1750)

    Another copy. [Without title]   It. 760
                                                                        score.
    B. g 3.   23x30.5cm. 10 st.
                                                                        WM: 73.
                                                                        Hand B³. Brown.

Another copy. [Sonata 1]   In Collection no. 2.   It. 694.

B. g 3.

57. No: 21 / Sonata / a Violino e Basso / Del Sig^r: / Giuseppe   It. 761
Tartini /   score.
                                                                         23.5x30.5cm. 10 st.
    Largo   WM: 14A.
    [Allegro]   Hand B^1. Black.
    Allegro assai

B. g 4.
Embellished version of Largo: It. 988:72, It. 1012:10.
Bass figured.
Published as no.1 of Opus II (Amsterdam, Le Cene, 1743)

58. Sonata a Violino, e Basso / Del / Sig^r: Giuseppe Tartini /   It. 762
                                                                         score.
    Largo   23x31.5cm. 10 st.
    Allegro   WM: 56.
    Andante - Allegro assai   Hand B. Black.

B. g 5.
Version with double stops.

Another copy. No: 11 / Sonata a Violino e Basso Del Sig:^r   It. 763
Giuseppe Tartini /   score.
                                                                         23.5x31.5cm. 10 st.
B. g 5.   WM: 74.
Caption title.   Hand N. Brown.
Version with double stops.
Bass figured.

59. Sonata a Violino e Basso / Del / Sig^r: Giuseppe Tartini /   It. 764
                                                                         score.
    Andante   22.5x30.5cm. 10 st.
    Allegro   WM: 63A.
    Allegro   Hand A. Brown.

B. g 6.
Version with double stops.

Another copy. No: 34 / Sonata / a / Violino, e Basso / Del   It. 765
Sig:^r / Giuseppe Tartini /   score.
                                                                         22.5x31cm. 10 st.
B. g 6.   WM: 62.
Version with double stops.   Hand B^2. Black.

Another copy. [Without title]   It. 766

B. g 6.   score.
Version with double stops.   23x31cm. 10 st.
Fragments in another hand on last page.   WM: unclear.
                                                                  Hand B³. Black.

Sonata 7:ᵐᵃ. In Collection no.1. It. 693.

    Andante affettuoso
    Allegro assai
    Allegro assai

B. g 11.
Embellished version of Andante affettuoso: It. 988:66, It. 994:5.
Published as no.7 of Opus II (Rome, Cleton, 1745)

60. Sonata a Violino e Basso / Del / Sig:ʳ Giuseppe Tartini /   It. 767

    Largo   score.
    Allegro   22.5x31cm. 10 st.
    Allegro   WM: 75.
                                                                  Hand A. Brown.
B. g 12.

61. Sonata a Violino, e Basso / Del Sig:ʳ / Giuseppe Tartini /   It. 768

    Adagio   score.
    Allegro   23x32.5cm. 10 st.
    Allegro   WM: 5.
                                                                  Hand B. Black.
B. g 13.

Another copy. Sonata a Violino Solo e Basso / No: 7 /   It. 769

B. g 13.   score.
Caption title.   23x31.5cm. 10 st.
Bass figured.   WM: 71.
                                                                  Hand N¹. Brown.

[Without title] In Collection no.2. It. 694.

    Allegro

B. g 14. Brainard gives three additional movements.

A major

62. No: 45 / Sonata a Violino e Basso / Del / Sig:ʳ Giuseppe
    Tartini /

    Andante
    Allegro
    Allegro assai
    Allegro
    Variazioni allegro (B. A 29e)

    B. A 1. Brainard gives two additional movements.
    Version with double stops.

It. 770
score.
22.5x30.5cm. 8 st.
WM: 71.
Hand A. Black.

63. Sonata a Violino, e Basso / Del / Sigʳ: Giuseppe Tartini /

    Largo andante
    Allegro
    Allegro
    Allegro assai

    B. A 1. Brainard gives two additional movements.

It. 771
score.
22.5x30.5cm. 10 st.
WM: 71.
Hand A. Black.

64. Sonata a Violino e Basso / Del / Sig:ʳ Giuseppe Tartini /

    Andante
    Allegro
    Allegro

    B. A 3.
    Published as no. 5 of Opus I (Amsterdam, Witvogel, 1732)

It. 772
score.
23x31.5cm. 10 st.
WM: 12.
Hand A. Brown.

65. Sonata à Violino, e Basso / Del / Sig.ʳ Giuseppe Tartini /
    Composta dal Medes.ᵐᵒ / Sopra lo stile che suona / il Prette
    dalla Chittara / Portoghese /

    Allegro
    Andante
    Allegro
    Minuetto

    B. A 4.

It. 773
score.
23x32cm. 12 st.
WM: 63A.
Hand A. Brown.

66. No: 19 / Sonata / A / Violino, e Basso / Del Sig:ʳ Giuseppe   It. 774
    Tartini /   score.
                                                                  23.5x30cm. 10 st.
        Largo   WM: 14A.
        Allegro   Hand Bˡ. Brown.
        [Allegro]

    B. A 5.
    Embellished version of Largo: It. 988:18.
    Published as no. 2 of Opus II (Amsterdam, Le Cene, 1743)

67. [Without title] No: 8 /   It. 775
                                                                  score.
        Adagio   23x30cm. 10 st.
        [Allegro]   WM: unclear.
        Allegro assai   Hand O. Brown.

    B. A 6.
    Bass figured.
    Published as no. 4 of Opus VI (Paris, Le Clerc, ca. 1748)

    Another copy. [Sonata] No. 6. In Collection no. 2. It. 694.

        Allegro
        Allegro assai

    B. A 6. Brainard gives one additional movement.

68. Sonata à Violino, e Basso / Del / Sig:ʳ Giuseppe Tartini /   It. 776
                                                                  score.
        Grave   23x32.5cm. 10 st.
        Allegro   WM: 68.
        Presto   Hand A. Brown.

    B. A 7.
    Caption title.

69. No: 14 / Sonata / a / Violino, e Basso / Del Sigʳ: / Giuseppe It. 777
    Tartini /   score.
                                                                  23x30cm. 10 st.
        Adagio   WM: unclear.
        [Allegro]   Hand Bˡ. Black.
        Presto

    B. A 9.
    Bass figured.

70. Sonata a Violino e Basso / Del / Sig:ʳ Giuseppe Tartini /   It. 778
                                                                        score.
        Andante cantabile   22x29.5cm. 8 st.
        Allegro   WM: 63A.
        Allegro assai   Hand A. Black.
        Allegro
        Presto

    B. A 10.and B. A 11. Brainard gives one additional movement
    for B. A 11.

71. Sonata a Violino, e Basso / Del / Sig:ʳ Giuseppe Tartini /   It. 779
                                                                        score.
        Andante   22x31cm. 10 st.
        Allegro   WM: 4.
        Presto   Hand A. Brown.

    B. A 12.

    [Sonata] No. 2. In Collection no. 2. It. 694.

        Adagio

    B. A 15. Brainard gives two additional movements.
    Published as no. 9 of Opus I (Amsterdam, Le Cene, 1734)

    Sonata 3:ᶻᵃ. In Collection no. 1. It. 693.

        Largo
        Allegro
        Presto

    B. A 17.
    Embellished version of Largo: It. 988:20.
    Published as no. 3 of Opus II (Rome, Cleton, 1745)

72. Del Sig:ʳ Tartini /   It. 780
                                                                        v part.
        [Adagio]   22x30cm. 12 st.
        Allegro ma non presto   WM: unclear.
        [Allegro]   Hand M¹. Brown.
                                                                        (completed in
    B. A 18.   another hand)

    Another copy. [Without title]   It. 781
                                                                        score.
        Largo andante   25.5x36.5cm. 10 st.
        Allegro non presto   WM: 66.
        [Allegro]   Hand G. Black.

    B. A 18.

73. Sonata a Violino, e Basso /

      Andante
      Allegro
      Allegro

    B. A 22. Brainard gives one additional movement.
    Incipit on t. p.

<u>It. 782</u>
score.
22.5x31.5cm. 10 st.
WM: 32 or 56.
Hand H. Brown.

74. Sonata a Violino, e Basso / Del / Sig.^{r} Giuseppe Tartini /

      Allegretto
      Andante
      Largo
      Presto

    B. A 24.

<u>It. 783</u>
score.
23x31.5cm. 8 st.
WM: 76.
Hand A. Brown.

75. Sonata à Violino, e Basso Del Sig:^{r} Giuseppe Tartini /

      Grave
      Allegro
      Allegro assai

    B. A 27.
    Caption title.

<u>It. 784</u>
score.
23.5x32.5cm. 10 st.
WM: 36.
Hand A. Brown.

76. Sonata à Violino, e Basso Del Sig.^{r} Giuseppe Tartini /

      Andante cantabile
      Allegro
      Largo
      Gavotta. Allegro non presto

    B. A 28.
    Caption title.

<u>It. 785</u>
score.
23.5x32cm. 10 st.
WM: 36.
Hand A. Brown.

77. Variazioni a Violino, e Basso / Del / Sig:^{r} Giuseppe Tartini /

      Variazioni

    B. A 29d.

<u>It. 786</u>
score.
22.5x29.5cm. 8 st.
WM: unclear.
Hand A. Brown.

78. Sonata à Violino e Basso: / No: 2 /

    Grave
    Allegro ma non presto
    Allegro

    B. A 30.
    Caption title.
    Fragment in another hand on last page.

It. 787
score.
21.5x27.5cm. 10 st.
WM: unclear.
Hand E. Black.

<u>A minor</u>

79. Sonata a Violino e Basso / Del Sig:ʳ Giuseppe Tartini /

    Adagio
    Variazione

    B. a 1. Brainard gives two additional movements.

It. 788
score.
21.5x30.5cm. 10 st.
WM: 63A.
Hand A. Brown.

80. Sonata a Violino, e Basso / Del / Sig:ʳ Giuseppe Tartini /

    Adagio
    Allegro
    Allegro

    B. a 4.

It. 789
score.
22x31.5cm. 10 st.
WM: 6.
Hand A. Brown.

81. Sonata a Violino e Basso / Del / Sig:ʳ Giuseppe Tartini /

    Largo
    Allegro
    Allegro assai

    B. a 6.

It. 790
score.
23.5x32cm. 10 st.
WM: unclear.
Hand A. Brown.

82. No: 30 / Sonata / a Violino, e Basso / Del Sigʳ: / Giuseppe Tartini /

    Andante
    Allegro
    Presto

    B. a 7.
    Bass figured.
    Published as no.4 of Opus VII (Paris, Maupetit, ca.1750)

It. 791
score.
23.5x30.5cm. 10 st.
WM: 14A.
Hand B¹. Black.

<u>Another copy.</u> [Sonata] No.4. In Collection no.2. <u>It.694.</u>

    B. a 7.

83. Sonata à Violino, e Basso Del Sig.ʳ Giuseppe Tartini /   It. 792
                                                                    score.
    Grave   23.5x32cm. 10 st.
    Allegro   WM: 36.
    Allegro   Hand A. Brown.

    B. a 8. Brainard gives three additional movements.
    Caption title.

84. Sonata à Violino, e Basso Del Sig.ʳ Giuseppe Tartini /   It. 793
                                                                    score.
    Grave   23.5x32.5cm. 10 st.
    Allegro   WM: 36.
    Allegro molto   Hand A. Brown.

    B. a 8. Brainard gives three additional movements.
    Caption title.

    Son: 5:ᵗᵃ. In Collection no.1. It.693.

       . [Andante cantabile]
       Allegro
       Allegro

    B. a 10.
    Published as no.5 of Opus II (Rome, Cleton, 1745)

85. Sonata a Violino e Basso / Del / Sig:ʳ Giuseppe Tartini /   It. 794
                                                                    score.
    Andante   23x31.5cm. 10 st.
    Allegro   WM: 12.
    Allegretto   Hand A. Brown.

    B. a 12.

86. Del Sig:ʳ Giuseppe Tartini /   It. 795
                                                                    score.
    Allegro   22.5x32cm. 10 st.
                                                                    WM: 68.
    B. a 13b.   Hand H. Brown.
    Caption title.
    With fingering.

<u>B flat major</u>

87. No. 50 / Sonata a Violino e Basso / Del / Sig:^r Giuseppe
Tartini /

    Largo
    Allegro
    Affettuoso
    Minuet

    B. B 1.

<u>It. 796</u>
score.
22.5x30.5cm. 8 st.
WM: 71.
Hand A. Black.

88. Sonata a Violino, e Basso / Del / Sig:^r Giuseppe Tartini /

    Andante cantabile
    Allegro
    Allegro

    B. B 3.
Embellished version of Andante cantabile: <u>It. 1010</u>:5.

<u>It. 797</u>
score.
22.5x30.5cm. 8 st.
WM: 16.
Hand A. Brown.

89. Sonata a Violino, e Basso / Del Sig:^r Giuseppe Tartini /

    Adagio
    Allegro
    Allegro
    Variazioni allegro

    B. B 5.
Caption title.
Version with double stops.
Published as no. 5 of Opus VI (Paris, Le Clerc, ca. 1748)

<u>It. 798</u>
score.
23x32cm. 10 st.
WM: 3.
Hand A. Brown.

<u>Another copy</u>. No: 10 / [Without title]

    Adagio
    Allegro
    Allegro

    B. B 5. Brainard gives one additional movement.
Version with double stops.

<u>It. 799</u>
score.
23.5x31.5cm. 10 st.
WM: 85.
Hand N. Brown.

<u>Another copy</u>. [Without title]

    Allegro

    B. B 5. Brainard gives three additional movements.

<u>It. 800</u>
score.
22.5x32cm. 10 st.
WM: 32.
Hand H. Brown.

90. Sonata a Violino, e Basso / Del / Sig.^{r} Giuseppe Tartini /

    Andante
    Variazioni
    Allegro assai

    B. B 6. Brainard gives one additional movement.

It. 801
score.
22x30.5cm. 8 st.
WM: 17.
Hand A. Brown.

91. Sonata a Violino e Basso / Del / Sig:^{r} Giuseppe Tartini /

    Grave
    Allegro
    Allegro

    B. B 8.
    Published as no. 6 of Opus I (Amsterdam, Witvogel, 1732)

It. 802
score.
23x32cm. 10 st.
WM: 12.
Hand A. Brown.

    Sonata 9:^{na}. In Collection no. 1. It. 693.·

    Largo andante
    Allegro
    Allegro

    B. B 9.
    Embellished version of Largo andante: It. 988:68, It. 994:8.
    Published as no. 9 of Opus II (Rome, Cleton, 1745)

92. Sonata a Violino e Basso / Del / Sig:^{r} Giuseppe Tartini /

    Adagio
    Andante
    Andante
    Giga

    B. B 11. Brainard gives one additional movement.
    Published as no. 2 of Opus V (Paris, Hue, ca. 1748)

It. 803
score.
23x31.5cm. 10 st.
WM: 12.
Hand A. Brown.

93. Variazioni / Del / Sig:^{r} Giuseppe Tartini /

    Variazioni

    B. B 13b.

It. 804
score.
23x31.5cm. 10 st.
WM: 4.
Hand A. Black.

94. No: 20 / [Without title]

    ...
    Allegro
    Affettuoso
    Andante

    B. B 14.

It. 805
score.
23.5x31cm. 10 st.
WM: unclear.
Hand G. Black.

B minor

95. Sonata a Violino, e Basso / Del / Sig:ʳ Giuseppe Tartini /   It. 806
                                                                        score.
    Largo andante   22.5x30.5cm. 10 st.
    Allegro   WM: 4.
    Allegro   Hand A. Brown.

    B. h 2.

96. Sonata a Violino, e Basso / Del / Sig:ʳ Giuseppe Tartini /   It. 807
                                                                        score.
    Largo   22.5x31cm. 10 st.
    Allegro   WM: 6.
    Allegro assai   Hand A. Brown.

    B. h 3.

97. Sonata a Violino e Basso / Del / Sig:ʳ Giuseppe Tartini /   It. 808
                                                                        score.
    Largo   23x31cm. 10 st.
    Allegro   WM: 22.
    Andante   Hand A. Brown.

    B. h 4.

    Sonata 4:ᵗᵃ. In Collection no.1. It.693.

    Andante
    Allegro
    Allegro

    B. h 6.
    Published as no.4 of Opus II (Rome, Cleton, 1745)

Trios

C major

1. Sonata a Trè / Del / Sig.^r Giuseppe Tartini / Basso /

It. 809
v 1 & 2, bass.
22.5x30.5cm. 10 st.
WM: 63A.
Hand A. Brown.

2. Sonata a Trè / Del / Sig:^r Giuseppe Tartini / Basso /

It. 810
v 1 & 2, bass.
22x30.5cm. 10 st.
WM: 63A.
Hand A. Brown.

D minor

3. Sonata a Tre / Del / Sig.^r Giuseppe Tartini / Basso /

It. 811
v 1 & 2, bass.
21.5x30cm. 10 st.
WM: unclear.
Hand A. Brown.

F major

4.   Sonata a Tre / Del / Sig.ʳ Giuseppe Tartini / Violino Primo /

It. 812
v 1 & 2, bass.
22x30.5cm. 10 st.
WM: 1.
Hand A.   Brown.

A major

5.   Sonata a Tre / Del / Sig.ʳ Giuseppe Tartini / Basso /

It. 813
v 1 & 2, bass.
22x30.5cm. 10 st.
WM: 1.
Hand A.   Brown.

6.   Sonata a Tre / Del / Sig.ʳ Giuseppe Tartini / Violino Primo /

It. 814
v 1 & 2, bass.
22x29.5cm. 10 st.
WM: 1.
Hand A.   Brown.

A minor

7.   Sonata a Tre / Del / Sig.ʳ Giuseppe Tartini / Basso /

It. 815
v 1 & 2, bass.
22x30cm. 10 st.
WM: 1.
Hand A.   Brown.

F major

8. Basso / Trio / Del Sig:^{r} Giuseppe Tartini /

It. 816
v 1& 2, bass.
22.5x32cm. 10 st.
WM: 4.
Hand A. Brown.

D major

9. Sinfonia a 3 / Del / Sig:^{r} Giuseppe Tartini / Violino P:^{mo} /

It. 817
v 1& 2, bass.
21.5x30cm. 8 st.
WM: 77.
Hand A. Brown.

10. Sinfonia a 3 / Del / Sig:^{r} Giuseppe Tartini / Violino P:^{mo} /

It. 818
v 1& 2, bass.
22.5x31cm. 8 st.
WM: 77A.
Hand A. Brown.

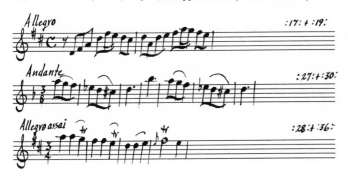

11. Sinfonia a 3 / Del / Sig:^r Giuseppe Tartini / Violino P:^{mo} /

It. 819
v 1 & 2, bass.
22.5x31.5cm. 8 st.
WM: 77 & 77A.
Hand A. Brown.

Title at end of last page.

12. Sinfonia a 3 / Del / Sig:^r Giuseppe Tartini / Violino P:^{mo} /

It. 820
v 1 & 2, bass.
22.5x30.5cm. 8 st.
WM: 77A.
Hand A. Brown.

F major

13. Sinfonia a 3 / Del / Sig:ʳ Giuseppe Tartini / Violino P:ᵐᵒ /

It. 821
v 1 & 2, bass.
23x31cm. 8 st.
WM: 77.
Hand A. Brown.

A major

14. Sinfonia a 3 / Del / Sigʳ Giuseppe Tartini / Basso /

It. 822
v 1 & 2, bass.
23x31.5cm. 10 st.
WM: unclear.
Hand A. Brown.

Allegro has same thematic material as the first Andante of
Tartini Sinfonia It. 823.

15. Sinfonia a 3 / Del / Sig:ʳ Giuseppe Tartini /

It. 823
v 1 & 2 [bass]
23x32cm. 10 st.
WM: 71.
Hand A. Black.

The first Andante has same thematic material as Allegro of
Tartini Sinfonia It. 822.

Quartets

D major

1. Sonata a Quattro / Del / Sig.ʳ Giuseppe Tartini / Basso /

It. 824
v 1 & 2, vla, bass.
22x31cm. 10 st.
WM: 53.
Hand A. Brown.

2. Sonata a Quattro / Del / Sig:ʳ Giuseppe Tartini / Basso /

It. 825
v 1 & 2, vla, bass.
22.5x31cm. 10 st.
WM: 32.
Hand A. Brown.

G major

3. Sinfonia a Quatro / Del / Sig:ʳ Giuseppe Tartini /

It. 826
v 1 & 2, vla [bass]
22x30.5cm. 8 st.
WM: 63A.
Hand A. Brown.

Concertos

C major

1. Violino Principale / Concerto / Del Sigʳ: / Giuseppe Tartini /

It. 827
vp, v 1 & 2 obl,
vla, bass.
22.5x32cm. 10 st.
WM: 53.
Hand B². Black.

    Allegro   C   116
    Adagio   12/8 :8:/:10:
    Allegro assai 2/4 271

D. 4.
Embellished version of Adagio: It. 988:62, It. 994:26, It. 995:26.

2. No: 30 / Violino Principale / Concerto / Del Sig[r]: Giuseppe
    Tartini /

        Allegro   ¢   154
        Largo andante   C   :7:/:8:
        Allegro   3/4   234

    D. 5.
    Embellished version of Largo andante: It. 989:24, It. 997:10,
    It. 1011:4.

It. 828
vp, v 1 & 2 obl,
vla, vlc obl.
23.5x31cm. 10 st.
WM: 78.
Hand B. Brown.

3. No: 43 / Violino Principale / Concerto / Del Sig[r]: Giuseppe
    Tartini /

        Allegro   C   :29:/:53/cadenza
        Largo andante   C   :9:/:10:
        Presto   2/4   :124:/156

    D. 6abc.
    Embellished version of Largo andante: It. 989:92, It. 999:6.
    Allegro is the same as the second Allegro of Alberghi Concerto
    It. 34, with differences in figuration.

It. 829
vp, v 1 & 2 obl,
vla, bass.
22.5x31cm. 8 st.
WM: 62.
Hand A[1]. Brown.
(title & cadenza
in Hand B)

4. No: 41 / Violino Principale / Concerto / Del Sig:[r] Giuseppe
    Tartini /

        Allegro assai   C   128
        Andante   C   31
        Presto   3/8   220

    D. 7.
    Incipit on t. p.
    Embellished version of Andante: It. 989:10, It. 994:32.

It. 830
vp, v 1 & 2 obl,
vla obl, vlc obl.
23x31cm. 10 st.
WM: 62 & 14A.
Hand A[1]. Black.
(v 1 in Hand I,
title in Hand B[1])

5. Violino Principale / Concerto / Del Sig[r]: Giuseppe Tartini /

        Allegro non molto   C   100
        Adagio   C   :8:/:8:
        Presto   2/4   271

    D. 8.
    Embellished version of Adagio: It. 989:48, It. 1000:6.

It. 831
vp, v 1 & 2 obl,
[vla obl] bass
obl.
23x30.5cm. 10 st.
WM: 14A.
Hand B[1]. Black.

6. Violino Principale / Concerto / Del / Sig:[r] Giuseppe Tartini /

        Allegro   C   :27:/:33
        Adagio   C   20
        Allegro   3/4   142

    D. 9.
    Embellished version of Adagio: It. 1011:6.

It. 832
vp, v 1 & 2 obl,
vla, bass.
22.5x31cm. 10 st.
WM: 79.
Hand C. Brown.

Another copy. Violino Principale / Concerto / Del Sig[r].   It. 833
Giuseppe Tartini /   vp.
                                                                23x29cm. 10 st.
D. 9.   WM: unclear.
Incipit on t. p.   Hand M. Brown.

7. Violino Principale / Concerto / Del Sig.[r] Giuseppe Tartini /   It. 834
                                                                vp, v 1 & 2 obl,
        Allegro   3/4   20/:5 1:/63   vla, bass.
        Andante   3/4   :16:/:16:   23x32cm. 10 st.
        Allegro   C   13/:25:/29   WM: 29.
                                                                Hand A. Brown.
    D. 11.
    Embellished version of Andante: It.989:52, It.1000:11, It.1001:10.

    Another copy. Violino Principale / Concerto / Del Sig:[r]   It. 835
    Giuseppe Tartini /   vp.
                                                                23x31.5cm. 10 st.
    D. 11.   WM: unclear.
    Incipit on t. p.   Hand H. Brown.

8. Violino Principale / Concerto / Del Sig:[r] Giuseppe Tartini /   It. 836
                                                                vp, v 1 & 2 obl,
        Allegro   C   :33:/45   vla, bass.
        Andante larghetto 12/8 :6:/:9:   22.5x30.5cm. 10 st.
        Allegro assai 3/4 :75:/99:   WM: 6.
                                                                Hand A. Brown.
    D. 12a bb c.
    Embellished version of Andante larghetto: It.989:60, It.996:6,
    It.1005:16.

9. Violino Principale / Concerto / Del Sig:[r] Giuseppe Tartini /   It. 837
                                                                vp, v 1 & 2 obl,
                                                                vla, bass.
                                                                22.5x31.5cm. 8 st.
                                                                WM: 69 & 53.
                                                                Hand A. Brown.

    - D. 12bb c.

10. Violino Principale / Concerto / Del Sig.ʳ Giuseppe Tartini /

      Allegro assai C   133
      Largo andante C   39
      Allegro 3/4 :20:/:42:/:69:

D. 13.
Embellished version of Largo andante: It. 989:80, It. 998:4.

> It. 838
> vp, v 1 & 2 obl,
> vla, bass.
> 22.5x31cm. 10 st.
> WM: 32 & 68.
> Hand A. Black.

11. Violino Principale / Concerto / Del Sig.ʳ Giuseppe Tartini /

      Allegro C   103
      Largo andante 3/4 :16:/:12:
      Allegro 3/4 126

D. 14c d, D. 5c.

> It. 839
> vp, v 1 & 2 obl,
> vla, vlc obl.
> 22.5x31cm. 10 st.
> WM: 68.
> Hand A. Brown.

12. No: 50 / Violino Principale / Concerto / Del / Sig:ʳ Giuseppe Tartini /

      Allegro 2/4 :88:/108/cadenza
      Andante largo 3/8 :24:/28
      Allegro C :31:/39/cadenza

D. 14a b e.

> It. 840
> vp, v 1 & 2 obl,
> vla, bass.
> 22.5x31cm. 8 st.
> WM: 71.
> Hand A. Black.
> (cadenzas in
> Hand B)

D major

13. Violino Principale / Concerto / Del Sig:ʳ Giuseppe Tartini /

      Allegro 3/4 328
      Cantabile C 20
      Allegro 12/8 132

D. 15.
Published as no. 4 of Opera prima, Libro primo (Amsterdam,
Le Cene, 1728)

> It. 841
> vp, v 1 & 2 obl,
> vla obl, vlc obl.
> 23x31.5cm. 10 st.
> WM: 76, 80, 3A
> & 36.
> Hand A. Brown.

14. Violino Principale / Concerto / Del Sigʳ: Giuseppe Tartini /

      [Allegro] C 123
      Adagio C :7:/:8:
      Allegro 2/4 241

D. 17a bb c.

> It. 842
> vp, v 1 & 2 obl,
> vla, vlc obl,
> organ.
> 22.5x31cm. 10 st.
> WM: 77A & 14A.
> Hand B². Black.

Another copy. No: 9 / Concerto / À più Strumenti / Del Sig.   It. 843
Giuseppe Tartini / Violino Principale /   vp, v 1 & 2 obl,
                                                                     vla, vlc obl,
D. 17abbc.   bass rip.
Incipit on t. p. No: 9 in Hand J.   22x30cm. 10 st.
                                                                     WM: 81.
                                                                     Hand J. Brown.

15. Violino Principale / Concerto / Del Sig^r: / Giuseppe Tartini /   It. 844
                                                                     vp.
     Allegro   3/4   216   23x30.5cm. 10 st.
     Grave   C   20   WM: 14A.
     Allegro   2/4   254   Hand B^l. Black.

     D. 19.
     Embellished version of Grave: It. 988:84, It. 994:38.

16. No: 11 / Violino Principale / Concerto / Del / Sig^r: Giuseppe   It. 845
     Tartini /   vp, v 1 & 2 obl,
                                                                     vla, vlc obl (2
     Allegro   C   115   copies)
     Grave   C   :8:/:10:   23x31.5cm. 10 st.
     Allegro   3/4   258   WM: 50 & 14A.
                                                                     Hand A. Black.
     D. 20.   (vlc part in Hand
     Grave is the same as that of D. 61.   N)
     Embellished version of Grave: It. 988:92.

17. Violino Principale / Concerto / Del Sig:^r Giuseppe Tartini /   It. 846
                                                                     vp, v 1 & 2 obl,
     Allegro   C   131   vla, vlc obl (2
     Grave   3/4   59   copies)
     Allegro   2/4   277   23x30cm. 10 st.
                                                                     WM: 14A & 62.
     D. 21.   Hand H^l. Black.
     Incipit on t. p.   (parts in Hand N)
     Embellished version of Grave: It. 988:44.

18. Violino Principale / Concerto / Del Sig.^r Giuseppe Tartini /   It. 847
                                                                     vp, v 1 & 2 obl,
     Allegro   C   104   vla, bass.
     Andante ma largo   C   42   22.5x31cm. 10 st.
     Allegro assai   2/4   258 /[capriccio 28] /17   WM: unclear.
                                                                     Hand A. Brown.
     D. 22.
     Andante ma largo is the same as Andante of D. 28.
     Embellished version of Andante ma largo: It. 989:14, It. 994:36.

<u>Another copy</u>. No: 45 / Violino Principale / Concerto / Del   It. 848
Sig:ʳ Giuseppe Tartini /   vp, v 1 & 2 obl,
                                                                            vla, bass.
D. 22.   23x31cm. 10 st.
                                                                            WM: 62.
                                                                            Hand A. Black.

19. Violino Principale / Concerto / Del Sig:ʳ Giuseppe Tartini /   It. 849
                                                                            vp, v 1 & 2 obl,
     Allegro   C   105 /cadenza   v 1 & 2 rip, vla
     Andante mà larghetto   12/8   32   (2 copies) vlc obl,
     Presto   3/8   :97:/132/cadenza   bass (3 copies)
                                                                            23x32cm. 10 st.
D. 23abc.   WM: 85 & 77.
Embellished version of Andante mà larghetto: It.988:42, It.989:   Hand D. Brown.
88, It.998:2, It.1015:1.

20. <u>Another copy</u>. No: 49 / Violino Principale / Concerto / Del / It. 850
Sig:ʳ Giuseppe Tartini /   vp, v 1 & 2 obl,
                                                                            vla, vlc obl.
D. 23abc.   22x30.5cm. 10 &
                                                                            8 st.
                                                                            WM: 19A & 71.
                                                                            Hand A. Brown.

20. Violino Principale / Concerto / Del / Sig:ʳ Giuseppe Tartini /   It. 851
                                                                            vp, v 1 & 2 obl,
     Allegro nòn presto   C   105   vla, vlc obl.
     Andante assai   2/4   118   22.5x31cm. 10 st.
     Allegro assai   3/4   20/:54:/72   WM: 53 & 64?
                                                                            Hand A. Brown.
D. 23ade.

21. Violino principale / Concerto / Del Sig.ʳ Giuseppe Tartini /   It. 852
                                                                            vp, v 1 & 2 obl,
     Allegro   3/4   20/:54:/72   vla, vlc obl.
     Andante assai   2/4   118   22x31.5cm. 10 st.
     Allegro assai   2/4   254   WM: 29.
                                                                            Hand A. Brown.
D. 23ed, D. 19c.

22. Violino Principale / Concerto / Del Sig:ʳ Giuseppe Tartini /

-- D. 23e.
Embellished version of Largo: It. 989:64, It. 999:7.

It. 853
vp, v 1 & 2 obl,
vla, bass.
22x31cm. 10 st.
WM: 4.
Hand A. Brown.

23. No: 46 / Violino Principale / Concerto / Del Sig:ʳ Giuseppe
Tartini /

       Allegro assai   3/4   217
       Adagio   C   33
       Presto   2/4   :96:/136

D. 24.
Embellished version of Adagio: It. 988:78, It. 995:20, It. 1010:3.

It. 854
vp, v 1 & 2 obl,
vla, bass.
22x30.5cm. 10 &
8 st.
WM: unclear &
62.
Hand A. Black.

24. No: 34 / Violino Principale / Concerto / del Sigʳ: Giuseppe
Tartini /

       Allegro   C   108
       Grave   C   :10:/:10:
       Allegro   3/8   258

D. 26.
Embellished version of Grave: It. 988:56, It. 994:17, It. 1010:4.

It. 855
vp, v 1 & 2 obl,
vla, vlc obl.
22.5x30.5cm. 10 st.
WM: 77 & 27A.
Hand A. Brown.
(title in Hand B)

25. No: 47 / Violino Principale / Concerto / Del / Sig:ʳ Giuseppe
Tartini /

       Allegro   C   100
       Andante   3/4   41/da capo 26
       Allegro   2/4   :86:/118

D. 27a bb c.
Embellished version of Andante: It. 989:74, It. 998:8, It. 1011:7.

It. 856
vp, v 1 & 2 obl,
vla obl, bass.
23x30cm. 8 &
10 st.
WM: unclear &
27A.
Hand A. Black.

26. No: 37 / Violino Principale / Concerto / Del Sig:^r Giuseppe Tartini /

    Allegro   C   110
    Andante cantabile   C   40
    Allegro assai   3/4   :66:/100

D. 28.
Incipit on t.p.
Andante cantabile is the same as Andante ma largo of D.22.
Embellished version of Andante cantabile: It.989:14, It.994:36.

It. 857
vp, v 1 & 2 obl
[vla obl, vlc obl]
23x32cm. 10 st.
WM: 62 & unclear.
Hand A¹. Black.
(title in Hand B¹)

27. Violino Principale / Concerto / Del Sig^r: / Giuseppe Tartini /

    Allegro   C   97
    Largo   12/8   :9:/:12:
    Allegro   2/4   212

D. 29.
Incipit on t.p.
Embellished version of Largo: It.988:4.

It. 858
vp, v 1 obl, vla,
[bass]
22.5x30cm. 10 st.
WM: unclear.
Hand B¹. Black.

Another copy. [Without title]

D. 29.

It. 859
vp [inc] v 1 obl.
23x30.5cm. 10 st.
WM: 3B.
Hand G. Brown.

28. Violino Principale / Concerto / Del Sig.^r Giuseppe Tartini /

    Allegro   ¢   20/:44:/:59:
    Andante   C   :10:/:10:
    Allegro   3/4   26/:54:/72

D. 30abbc.
Embellished version of Andante: It.989:32, It.997:12, It.1010:7.

It. 860
vp, v 1 & 2 obl,
vla, bass.
22.5x31cm. 10 st.
WM: 4.
Hand A. Brown.

29. Violino Principale / Concerto / Del Sig:^r Giuseppe Tartini /

    Allegro   C   83
    Andante   C   :8:/:8:
    Allegro assai   2/4   128

D. 31abbc.
Embellished version of Andante: It.988:82, It.994:15, It.995:15, It.1001:2.

It. 861
vp, v 1 & 2 obl,
vla, bass.
23x31cm. 8 st.
WM: 16.
Hand A. Brown.

30. No: 26 / Violino Principale / Concerto / Del / Sig:^r Giuseppe
    Tartini /

      Allegro C 95
      Grave   C :7:/:10:
      Allegro 2/4 227

D. 32.
Embellished version of Grave: It. 988:36.

It. 862
vp, v 1 & 2 obl,
vla, bass.
22.5x30cm. 10 st.
WM: 86 & 14.
Hand A. Black.

Another copy. Violino Principale / Concerto / Del Sig:^r
Giuseppe Tartini /

D. 32.
Incipit on t. p.

It. 863
vp.
23x30.5cm. 10 st.
WM: 14.
Hand H¹. Brown.
(title in Hand B)

---

31. Concerto / del Sig^r: Giuseppe Tartini /

      Allegro C 64/cadenza 14/4
      Andante 3/4 35
      Allegro C 11/:19:/37

D. 33.
Incipit on t. p.
Embellished version of Andante: It. 989:34, It. 997:14, It. 1002:2.

It. 864
vp, v 1 & 2 obl,
vla, bass.
23x32cm. 10 st.
WM: unclear & 87.
Hand H². Brown.

Another copy. Violino Principale / Concerto / Del Sig:^r
Giuseppe Tartini /

D. 33.

It. 865
vp.
23x32cm. 10 st.
WM: 98.
Hand B. Black.

---

32. Violoncello Obbligato / Concerto / Del Sig^r: / Giuseppe
    Tartini /

      Allegro C 116
      Grave   3/4 :12:/:15:
      Allegro 2/4 247/capriccio 70

D. 34.
Embellished version of Grave: It. 989:22, It. 997:2, It. 1010:1.

It. 866
vp, v 1 & 2 obl,
vla obl, vlc obl.
23x32cm. 10 st.
WM: 73 & 64.
Hand B². Black.

---

33. Violino Principale / Concerto / Del Sig.^r Giuseppe Tartini /

      Allegro C 70
      Andante 3/4 :16:/19
      Allegro 2/4 :54:/70

D. 35.
Embellished version of Andante: It. 989:28, It. 997:4, It. 1011:3.

It. 867
vp, v 1 & 2 obl,
vla, bass.
22.5x31cm. 10 st.
WM: 4.
Hand A. Brown.

34. Violino Principale / Concerto / Del Sig.^r Giuseppe Tartini /

      Allegro 3/4 :58:/62
      Larghetto C :8:/10
      Allegro C :27:/32

  D. 36.
Embellished version of Larghetto: It. 988:96, It. 989:90, It. 995:6, It. 999:13.

It. 868
vp, v 1 & 2 obl,
vla, bass.
22x31.5cm. 10 st.
WM: 4.
Hand A. Brown.

35. Violino Principale / Concerto / Del Sig.^r Giuseppe Tartini /

      Allegro C :25:/37
      Andante 3/4 :12:/:16:
      Allegro non presto 12/8 :11:/:27:/29

  D. 37.
Embellished version of Andante: It. 989:72, It. 999:15.

It. 869
vp, v 1 & 2 obl,
vla, bass.
22x31cm. 10 st.
WM: 4.
Hand A. Brown.

36. Violino Principale / Pastorale / Del Sig:^r / Giuseppe Tartini /

      Allegro assai 2/4 235
      Adagio 12/8 :9:/:8:
      Allegro assai 3/8 225/ [capriccio] 34(12/8)/23 (2/4)

  D. 38.
Embellished version of Adagio : It. 988:40, It. 1004:2.

It. 870
vp, v 1 & 2 obl,
vla, bass.
23x30.5cm. 10 st.
WM: unclear & 14A.
Hand B¹. Black.

37. Violino Principale / Concerto / Del Sig.^r Giuseppe Tartini /

      Allegro assai C 18/:44:/55
      Andante 3/4 :24:/22
      Allegro 3/4 :53:/56/capriccio 32/8

  D. 39.
Embellished version of Andante: It. 988:50, It. 995:22.

It. 871
vp, v 1 & 2 obl,
vla, bass.
22.5x31.5cm. 10 st.
WM: 4 & unclear.
Hand A. Brown.

38. Violino Principale / Concerto / Del Sig:^r Giuseppe Tartini /

      Allegro C :36:/50
      Andante C :16:/:17:
      Allegro 3/4 :74:/86

  D. 40.

It. 872
vp, v 1 & 2 obl,
vla, bass.
22x31.5cm. 10 st.
WM: 28 & unclear.
Hand A. Brown.

39. Violino Principale / Concerto / Del Sig.^r Giuseppe Tartini /

    Allegro   ¢ :44:/66
    Largo andante   C :6:/:8:
    Presto   2/4   32/:68:/80

    D. 41.
    Embellished version of Largo andante: It.989:18, It.995:4,
    It.1005:5.

It. 873
vp, v 1 & 2 obl,
vla, bass.
22x30cm. 10 st.
WM: unclear.
Hand A. Brown.

40. Violino Principale / Concerto / Del Sig:^r Giuseppe Tartini /

    Presto   ¢   18/:46:/62
    Larghetto   3/4 :16:/:20:
    Allegro assai   2/4   44/:71:/92

    D. 42.
    Embellished version of Larghetto: It.1001:8, It.1005:1.

It. 874
vp, v 1 & 2 obl,
vla, bass.
22x31cm. 10 &
8 st.
WM: 83 & unclear.
Hand A. Brown.

41. Concerto a Quattro / Violino Principale / Concerto / Del Sig.^r
Giuseppe Tartini /

    Allegro   C   90
    Grave   C   29
    Allegro   2/4   69

    D. Anh. IV.
    According to Dounias, by Gasparo Visconti.
    Published as no. 11 of Opera´primo, Libro terzo (Amsterdam,
    Le Cene, ca. 1730)

It. 875
vp, v 1 rip, v 2
con, vlc obl.
22x30.5cm. 8 &
10 st.
WM: 76.
Hand A. Brown.

D minor

42. Violino Principale / Concerto / Del Sig^r: Giuseppe Tartini /

    Allegro   2/4   279
    Grave   3/4   77
    Allegro   2/4   186

    D. 44.
    Embellished version of Grave: It.989:46, It.992:2, It.1000:2.

It. 876
vp, v 1 & 2 obl,
vla, vlc obl.
23x30.5cm. 10 st.
WM: 62.
Hand B^2. Black.

43. Violino Principale / Concerto / Del Sig:^r Giuseppe Tartini /

    Allegro   3/4 :77:/87
    Grave   C :8:/:10:
    Presto   2/4   32/:84:/96

    D. 45.
    Embellished version of Grave: It.989:50, It.1000:8, It.1011:2.

It. 877
vp, v 1 & 2 obl,
vla, bass.
22x31cm. 10 st.
WM: 83.
Hand A. Brown.

E major

44. Violino Principale / Concerto / Del Sig:ʳ Giuseppe Tartini /

          Allegro   C   128
          Adagio   C   32
          Allegro assai   3/8   275/capriccio 43/8

   D. 47

It. 878
vp, v 1 & 2 obl,
vla obl, vlc obl.
23x31.5cm. 10 st.
WM: 28.
Hand A. Black.

45. Violino Principale / Concerto / Del Sig:ʳ Giuseppe Tartini /

          Allegro   C   123
          Largo   3/4   44
          Allegro   2/4   218/capriccio 33/10

   D. 48.

It. 879
vp, v 1 & 2 obl,
vla obl, vlc obl.
22.5x31.5cm. 10 st.
WM: 29 & 6.
Hand A. Brown.

46. No: 40 / Violino Principale / Concerto / Del Sig:ʳ Giuseppe
Tartini /

          Allegro assai   C   107
          Grave   C   :7:/:9:
          Presto   3/8   215

   D. 50.
   Incipit on t.p.

It. 880
vp, v 1 & 2 obl,
vla obl, vlc obl.
23x32cm. 10 st.
WM: unclear.
Hand A¹. Brown.
(title in Hand B¹,
vlc obl in another
hand)

47. Violino Principale / Concerto / Del Sig:ʳ Giuseppe Tartini /

It. 881
vp, v 1 & 2 obl,
vla obl, vlc obl.
23x31.5cm. 10 st.
WM: 76, 58 & 3A.
Hand A. Brown.

   Autograph Padova Ms. D VI. 1893.
   Belongs stylistically to Period I.

48. Concerto a Solo / Del Sig:^r / Giuseppe Tartini /

       Allegro   C   104
       Largo   12/8 :8:/:9:
       Allegro   3/8   216

D. 51.
Incipit on t. p.
Embellished version of Largo: It. 988:38.

It. 882
vp, v 1 & 2 obl,
vla, bass.
23x30cm. 10 st.
WM: 14A.
Hand B^1. Brown.
(v 1 & 2 obl in
Hand H^1)

Another copy. Violino Principale / Concerto / Del Sig:^r
Giuseppe Tartini /

D. 51.

It. 883
vp.
23x31.5cm. 10 st.
WM: 98.
Hand B. Black.

---

49. Violino Principale / Concerto / Del Sig:^r Giuseppe Tartini /

       Allegro   C   80
       Andante 3/4 :16:/:16:
       Allegro assai 2/4 24/:48:/68

D. 53.
Embellished version of Andante: It. 988:52, It. 994:16, It. 995:2.

It. 884
vp, v 1 & 2 obl,
vla, bass.
22.5x31.5cm. 10 st.
WM: 6.
Hand A. Brown.

---

50. [Without title]

       Allegro ¢ 20/:41:/48
       Andante 3/4 :12:/14
       Presto 2/4 :84:/106

D. 54.
Embellished version of Andante: It. 988:90.

It. 885
v 2 obl.
22x29.5cm. 10 st.
WM: unclear.
Hand A. Brown.

E minor

51. Violino Principale / Concerto / Del Sig:^r Giuseppe Tartini /

       Allegro   C   187
       Grave   3/4 :15:/:14:
       Allegro 12/8 132

D. 55.
Published as no. 2 of Opera prima, Libro primo (Amsterdam,
Le Cene, 1728)

It. 886
vp, v 1 & 2 obl,
vla, vlc obl.
23x32cm. 10 st.
WM: 28.
Hand A. Brown.

52. [Without title]

      [Allegro]   C   221
      Adagio 12/8 :8:/:8:
      [Allegro] 2/4 251

   D. 56.

It. 887
[vp] v 1 & 2 obl,
vla obl, vlc obl.
23x30.5cm. 10 st.
WM: unclear.
Hand B^2. Black.

F major

53. Violino Principale / Concerto / Del Sig:^{r} Giuseppe Tartini /

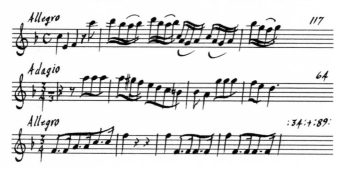

D. 58a‑c.
Published with a different Adagio as no.5 of Opera prima,
Libro primo (Amsterdam, Le Cene, 1728)

It. 888
vp, v 1 & 2 obl,
vla obl, vlc obl.
23x32cm. 8 &
10 st.
WM: 76 & 36.
Hand A. Brown.

54. Violino Principale / Concerto / Del Sig:^{r} Giuseppe Tartini /

      Allegro C   133
      Adagio C   34
      Allegro 3/4 177/capriccio 40/15

   D. 59.
Embellished version of Adagio: It.989:85, It.999:4.
Published as no.3 of Opera prima, Libro secondo (Amsterdam,
Le Cene, ca.1730)

It. 889
vp, v 1 & 2 obl,
vla, vlc obl.
23x32.5cm. 10 st.
WM: 3.
Hand A. Brown.

55. Violino Principale / Concerto / Del Sig^r: Giuseppe Tartini /

      Allegro C   140
      Grave   C :8:/:10:
      Allegro C   117

   D. 61.
Grave is the same as that of D. 20.
Embellished version of Grave: It.988:92, It.994:40.

It. 890
vp, v 1 & 2 obl,
vla obl, vlc obl,
bass (first move-
ment)
23x32cm. 10 st.
WM: unclear.
Hand E. Black.
(parts in Hands
L & F^1)

56. Violino Principale / Concerto / Del / Sig:ʳ Giuseppe Tartini /

      Allegro   C   88
      Grave   3/4   56
      Presto   3/8   :63:/:68:/8

    D. 63 a b c.
    Embellished version of Grave: It. 1016:1.

It. 891
vp, v 1 & 2 obl,
vla.
22.5x31cm. 10 st.
WM: 79 & unclear.
Hand C. Brown.

57. Violino Principale / Concerto / Del / Sig:ʳ Giuseppe Tartini /

      Allegro non presto   C   :32:/51
      Grave   C   :9:/:8:
      Presto   3/8   28/:89:/119

    D. 64.
    Embellished version of Grave: It. 1011:1.

It. 892
vp, v 1 & 2 obl,
vla, bass.
23x31.5cm. 10 st.
WM: 58.
Hand A. Black.

58. Violino Principale / Concerto / Del Sig:ʳ Giuseppe Tartini /

      Allegro   C   112
      Grave   C   :10:/:10:
      Presto   3/4   :48:/80

    D. 65.

It. 893
vp, v 1 & 2 obl,
vla obl, vlc obl.
23x32.5cm. 10 st.
WM: 98 & 27A.
Hand B. Black.
(parts in Hand A¹)

    <u>Another copy</u>. No: 42 / Violino Principale / Concerto / Del
Sig:ʳ Giuseppe Tartini /

    D. 65.
    Incipit on t. p.

It. 894
vp.
22.5x31.5cm. 10 st.
WM: 62.
Hand K. Black.

59. Violino Principale / Concerto / Del Sig:ʳ Giuseppe Tartini /

      Allegro   C   89
      Andante   2/4   :22:/:20:
      Allegro   2/4   24/:62:/98

    D. 66.
    Embellished version of Andante: It. 988:94, It. 995:7, It. 1001:6.

It. 895
vp, v 1 & 2 obl,
vla, bass.
22x31cm. 10 &
8 st.
WM: 83.
Hand A. Brown.

60. Violino Principale / Concerto / Del Sig:ʳ Giuseppe Tartini /

      Allegro assai   2/4   :99:/152
      Andante cantabile   12/8   :13:/13
      Allegro   3/4   :60:/68

    D. 67.
    Embellished version of Andante cantabile: It. 1003:3.

It. 896
vp, v 1 & 2 obl,
vla, vlc obl.
22.5x30cm. 10 st.
WM: 6.
Hand A. Brown.

61. Violino Principale / Concerto / Del Sig:[r] Giuseppe Tartini /

It. 897
vp, v 1 & 2 obl,
vla, bass.
22.5x29.5cm. 10 st.
WM: 14.
Hand A. Brown.

  Allegro assai C 97
  Andante   C :11:/:11:
  Presto   3/4   34/:68:/74

 D. 68.
Embellished version of Andante: It. 989:87, It. 999:8.

62. No: 35 / Violino Principale / Concerto / Del Sig:[r] Giuseppe
Tartini /

It. 898
vp, v 1 & 2 obl,
vla [bass]
23x31.5cm. 10 st.
WM: 73.
Hand B[2]. Black.

  Allegro   C   106
  Andante   2/4   :20:/:20:/10
  [Grave]   2/4   :20:/:20:
  Allegro   2/4   192 /cadenza

 D. 69.
Incipit on t. p.
Grave is a variant of Andante.
Embellished version of Andante: It. 988:34.

63. Violino Principale / Concerto / Del Sig:[r] Giuseppe Tartini /

It. 899
vp, v 1 & 2 obl,
vla, bass.
23x32cm. 10 st.
WM: 84.
Hand A. Brown.

  Allegro   3/4   :60:/60
  Andante   3/4   :16:/:16:
  Allegro   C   :28:/38? (incomplete)

 D. 70A, 70b c.
Embellished version of Andante: It. 989:30, It. 990:1, It. 997:6,
It. 1005:32, It. 1012:1.

64. Concerto / Del / Sig:[r] Giuseppe Tartini / 1768 /

It. 900
[vp] v 1 & 2 obl,
vla [vlc obl]
23x32cm. 10 st.
WM: 56.
Hand F. Brown.

Another copy. Violino Principale / Concerto / Del / Sig:[r]
Michiel Straticò / See It. 654.

G major

65. Violino Principale / Concerto / Del Sig:[r] Giuseppe Tartini /

      Allegro C   105/da capo 9
      Largo   3/4 79
      Allegro 2/4 120

D. 73.
Published as no.1 of Opus 2 (Amsterdam, Witvogel, ca.1733)

It. 901
vp, v 1 rip, v 2,
vla, organ.
23x32cm. 10 st.
WM: 64 & 77A.
Hand B[2]. Black.
(parts in Hand I[1])

66. Violino Principale / Concerto / Del / Sig:[r] Giuseppe Tartini /

      Allegro 3/4 238
      Grave   C   36
      Allegro 2/4 217/capriccio 48, adagio, unbarred/16

D. 75.
Embellished version of Grave: It. 988:88, It. 991:1, It. 1006:2.

It. 902
vp, v 1 & 2 obl,
vla, vlc obl.
22.5x31.5cm. 10 st.
WM: 75 & 15.
Hand A. Brown.

Another copy. No: 10 / Concerto / à piu Stromenti Obbl. [i] /
Del Sig: Giuseppe Tartini / Violino Principale /

D. 75.
Incipit on t.p. No: 10 in Hand J.

It. 903
vp, v 1 & 2 obl,
vla, vlc obl.
23x32cm. 10 st.
WM: 57 & unclear.
Hand J. Brown.

67. Violoncello Obbligato / Concerto / AS / Del Sig[r]: / Giuseppe
Tartini /

      Andante C   110
      Andante C   :11:/:16:
      Allegro 2/4 208

D. 76.
Embellished version of Andante, second movement: It. 988:30.

It. 904
vp, v 1 & 2 obl,
vla, vlc obl.
23.5x30.5cm. 10 st.
WM: unclear.
Hand B[2]. Black.

68. Violino Principale / Concerto / Del Sig[r]: / Giuseppe Tartini /

      Allegro C   114
      Adagio C   21
      Presto 2/4 153

D. 77.
Incipit on t.p.
Embellished version of Adagio: It. 1004:1.

It. 905
vp, v 1 & 2 obl,
vla obl, vlc obl.
23x30.5cm. 10 st.
WM: unclear & 14A.
Hand B[1]. Black.

69. Violino Principale / Concerto / Del Sig:ʳ Giuseppe Tartini /

   Allegro C 90
   Andante C :10:/:11:
   Presto 3/8 :76:/:86:/9

 D. 78.
 Incipit on t.p.
 Embellished version of Andante: It.988:32, It.1011:5.

It. 906
vp, v 1 & 2 obl,
vla, bass.
22.5x31cm. 10 st.
WM: 77A & 74.
Hand C. Brown.
(8 alternative
measures in Hand
B)

  Another copy. Violino Principale / Concerto / Del Sigʳ.
  Giuseppe Tartini /

  D. 78.
  Incipit on t.p.

It. 907
vp.
23x29.5cm. 10 st.
WM: unclear.
Hand M. Brown.

70. No: 39 / Violino Principale / Concerto / Del Sig:ʳ Giuseppe
Tartini /

   Allegro 3/4 204
   Andante 3/8 70
   Presto 2/4 :88:/:104:/8

 D. 79.
 Incipit on t.p.
 Embellished version of Andante: It.989:20, It.995:18.

It. 908
vp, v 1 & 2 obl,
vla obl, vlc obl.
22.5x32cm. 10 st.
WM: 14A.
Hand A¹. Brown.
(title & incipit in
Hand B¹)

71. Violino Principale / Concerto / Del Sigʳ: Giuseppe Tartini /

   Allegro non presto C 92
   Andante 2/4 :20:/:20:
   Allegro assai 3/8 24/:64:/ 56/ [capriccio] 38/16

 D. 80a bb c.
 Embellished version of Andante: It.989:58, It.1000:10.

It. 909
vp, v 1 & 2 obl,
vla, bass.
22.5x31.5cm. 8 st.
WM: 69.
Hand A. Black.

72. No: 44 / Violino Principale / Concerto / Del / Sig:ʳ Giuseppe
Tartini /

   Allegro assai 2/4 :84:/112
   Largo andante C :7:/10
   Allegro assai 3/4 :60:/92/capriccio 50/16

 D. 81.
 Incipit on t.p.
 Embellished version of Largo andante: It.989:8, It.992:1.

It. 910
vp, v 1 & 2 obl,
vla obl, vlc obl.
22.5x31.5cm. 10 st.
WM: 92.
Hand C. Brown.

73. Violino Principale / Concerto / Del Sig.^r Giuseppe Tartini /

      Allegro 3/4 170
      Andante 12/8 :8:/:10:
      Presto 2/4 :88:/:104:/8

    D. 82 a b, D. 79c.
    Embellished version of Andante: It.989:56, It.996:3.

> It. 911
> vp, v 1 & 2 obl,
> vla obl, bass.
> 22.5x29.5cm. 10 st.
> WM: 53.
> Hand A. Brown.

74. Violino Prinpale / Concerto / Del Sig:^r Giuseppe Tartini /

      Allegro C 91
      Andante C :8:/:8:
      Allegro 3/4 :56:/80

    D. 83.
    Embellished version of Andante: It.989:26, It.997:8.

> It. 912
> vp, v 1 & 2 obl,
> vla, vlc obl.
> 22.5x31.5cm. 8 &
> 10 st.
> WM: 69 & unclear.
> Hand A. Black.

75. Violino Principale / Concerto / Del Sig.^r Giuseppe Tartini /

      Allegro moderato C 73
      Andante cantabile 2/4 :16:/:20:
      Allegro assai 3/4 20/:52:/60

    D. 84.
    Embellished version of Andante cantabile: It.988:70, It.995:17.

> It. 913
> vp, v 1 & 2 obl,
> [vla] [bass]
> 21.5x30.5cm.
> 10 & 8 st.
> WM: unclear.
> Hand A. Brown.

76. No: 55 / Violino Principale / Concerto / Del / Sig:^r Giuseppe
    Tartini /

      Allegro 3/4 146
      Larghetto C :8:/:9:
      Allegro assai C :29:/44

    D. Anh. VII.
    Embellished version of Larghetto: It.988:74, It.991:1, It.995:11,
    It.1005:10.

> It. 914
> vp, v 1 & 2 obl,
> vla, bass.
> 23x30.5cm. 8 st.
> WM: 19.
> Hand A. Brown.

G minor

77. Violino Principale / Concerto / Del Sig:^r Giuseppe Tartini /
    Con Violoncello Obligato / 1766 /

      Allegro C 123
      Grave C 34
      Allegro 12/8 113

    D. 86.

> It. 915
> vp, v 1 & 2 obl,
> vla, vlc obl.
> 22x30.5cm. 10 st.
> WM: 4 & 80.
> Hand S. Brown.
> (last 2 lines of
> title & vla, Hand F)

Another copy. Violino Principale / Concerto / Del Sig:^r
Giuseppe Tartini /

D. 86.
Incipit on t.p.

It. 916
vp, v 1 & 2 obl,
v 1 & 2 rin, vla
rin, vlc obl, bass.
23x31cm. 10 st.
WM: 93.
Hand L. Brown.

78. No: 54 / Violino Principale / Concerto / Del / Sig:^r Giuseppe
Tartini /

     Allegro assai   2/4   256
     Largo andante   3/4   60
     Allegro   C   112

D. 87.
Embellished version of Largo andante: It. 988:48, It. 994:20,
It. 1005:3.

It. 917
vp, v 1 & 2 obl,
vla, bass.
22x31cm. 10 st.
WM: 64.
Hand A. Brown.

A major

79. Violino Principale / Concerto / Del Sig:^r Giuseppe Tartini /

     Allegro   C   132
     Largo andante   3/4   32/da capo 16
     Allegro   2/4   344

D. 88.
Published as no. 5 of Opera prima, Libro secondo (Amsterdam,
Le Cene, ca. 1730)

It. 918
vp, v 1 & 2 obl,
vla obl, vlc obl.
22.5x31.5cm. 10 st.
WM: 76 & 36.
Hand A. Brown.

80. Violino Principale / Concerto / Del Sig.^r Giuseppe Tartini /

     Allegro   C   179
     Adagio   C   27
     Presto   3/8   270/capriccio 60/16

D. 91.
Embellished version of Adagio: It. 989:82, It. 998:1.
Published as no. 2 of Opera prima, Libro secondo (Amsterdam,
Le Cene, ca. 1730)

It. 919
vp, v 1 & 2 obl,
vla obl, vlc obl,
contra basso obl.
23x32cm. 10 st.
WM: 29 & 4.
Hand A. Black.

Another copy. [Without title]

     Allegro   C   179
     Presto   3/8   270/capriccio 60/16

D. 91 a c.

It. 920
vp.
22.5x31cm. 10 st.
WM: 77A.
Hand B^2. Black.

81. Violino Principale / Pastorale / Del Sig:ʳ Giuseppe Tartini /

      Largo andante 12/8 24
      Allegro C 111
      Allegro 12/8 118

  D. 94.
  Incipit on t.p.

It. 921
vp.
23.5x30cm. 10 st.
WM: 14A.
Hand B¹. Black.

82. Violino Principale / Concerto / Del Sig:ʳ Giuseppe Tartini /

      Allegro C 111
      Andante larghetto C :8:/:10:
      Allegro assai 3/8 :68:/104

  D. 97.
  Embellished version of Andante larghetto: It. 989:70, It. 999:12,
  It. 1006:1.

It. 922
vp, v 1 & 2 obl,
vla obl, vlc obl.
22.5x31cm. 10 st.
WM: 69 & 53.
Hand A. Black.

83. Violino Principale / Concerto / Del Sig:ʳ Giuseppe Tartini /

      Allegro C 106
      Grave C :8:/:10:
      Allegro 2/4 272

  D. 99.
  Incipits on t.p. in Hands B¹ & G.
  Embellished version of Grave: It. 989:44, It. 996:2.

It. 923
vp [v 1 & 2 obl,
vla, bass]
23x30cm. 10 st.
WM: 14A.
Hand B¹. Brown.

Another copy. Violino Principale / Concerto / Del Sig:ʳ
Giuseppe Tartini /

  D. 99.

It. 924
vp.
23x31.5cm. 10 st.
WM: 98.
Hand B. Black.

84. No: 36 / Violino Principale / Concerto / Del Sig:ʳ Giuseppe
Tartini /

      Allegro C 95
      Andante 3/8 91
      Allegro 2/4 202

  D. 100.
  Embellished version of Andante: It. 989:42, It. 1000:4, It. 1011:8.

It. 925
vp, v 1 & 2 obl,
vla, vlc obl.
22.5x32cm. 10 st.
WM: unclear & 77A.
Hand A¹. Brown.
(title in Hand B)

85. No: 38 / Violino Principale / Concerto / Del Sig:^r Giuseppe
    Tartini /

      Allegro   C   112
      Andante cantabile   C   36/unbarred cadenza
      Allegro   2/4   218

    D. 101.
    Incipit on t.p.
    Embellished version of Andante cantabile: It.989:12, It.994:34.

It. 926
vp, v 1 & 2 obl,
vla obl, vlc obl.
23x31cm. 10 st.
WM: unclear, 14A
& 73.
Hand A¹. Brown.
(title & cadenza
in Hand B¹, vla &
vlc in Hand I)

    Another copy. Violino Principale / Concerto / Del Sig:^r Giuseppe
    Tartini /

    D. 101.
    Incipit on t.p.

It. 927
vp, v 1 & 2 obl,
vla obl, vlc obl.
22.5x31.5cm. 10 st.
WM: 94 & 95.
Hand D. Brown.
(parts in Hand F)

86. Violino Principale / Concerto / Del Sig:^r Giuseppe Tartini /

      Allegro assai   ¢   95
      Andante   12/8   22
      Allegro   6/8   68/capriccio 9(12/8)/8(6/8)

    D. 102.

It. 928
vp, v 1 & 2 obl,
[vla] bass.
22.5x31cm. 8 &
10 st.
WM: unclear.
Hand A. Brown.

87. No: 52 / Violino Principale / Concerto / Del Sig:^r Giuseppe
    Tartini /

      Allegro   C   105
      Grave   C   :9:/:9:
      Allegro assai   2/4   216/capriccio 10/8

    D. 103.
    Embellished version of Grave: It.988:80, It.994:30.

It. 929
vp, v 1 & 2 obl,
[vla] vlc obl.
23.5x32cm. 10 &
8 st.
WM: unclear & 19.
Hand A. Brown.

88. Violino Principale / Concerto / Del Sig:^r Giuseppe Tartini /

      Allegro   C   79
      Larghetto   3/4   :16:/:16:
      Allegro assai   2/4   32/:82:/78/cadenza 20

    D. 104.
    Embellished version of Larghetto: It.989:40, It.997:20,
    It.1006:3.

It. 930
vp, v 1 & 2 obl,
vla, bass.
22.5x31cm. 8 &
10 st.
WM: 69 & 53.
Hand A. Brown.

89. Violino Principale / Concerto / Del Sig:ʳ Giuseppe Tartini /   It. 931
                                                                           vp, v 1 & 2 obl,
     Allegro   C   109   vla, vlc obl.
     Larghetto 12/8 :8:/:11:   22.5x30.5cm. 8 &
     Presto   2/4   32/:62:/86   10 st.
                                                                           WM: 58 & 63.
  D. 106.   Hand A. Brown.
Embellished version of Larghetto: It. 989:66, It. 999:2.

90. Violino Principale / Concerto / Del Sig:ʳ Giuseppe Tartini /   It. 932
                                                                           vp, v 1 & 2 obl,
     Allegro non presto   C   97   vla, bass.
     Grave   C   :6:/:6:   22x30.5cm. 10 st.
     Allegro assai   3/4   20/:53:/:56:   WM: 69 & 53.
                                                                           Hand A. Brown.
  D. 107.
Embellished version of Grave: It. 989:68, It. 999:11, It. 1001:4.

91. Violino Principale / Concerto / Del Sig.ʳ Giuseppe Tartini /   It. 933
                                                                           vp, v 1 & 2 obl,
     Allegro   2/4   :84:/115   vla, bass.
     Largo   12/8   :10:/:12:   22x30cm. 10 st.
     Presto   3/8   :78:/109   WM: 67.
                                                                           Hand A. Brown.
  D. 108.
Embellished version of Largo: It. 988:64, It. 995:13, It. 1005:8.

92. Violino Principale / Concerto / Del Sig.ʳ Giuseppe Tartini /   It. 934
                                                                           vp, v 1 & 2 obl,
     Allegro   3/4   25/:51:/77   vla, bass, score
     Grave   C   :8:/8   of Grave.
     Allegro   C   12/:29:/33   22x31cm. 10 st.
                                                                           WM: 4 & 3.
  D. 109.   Hand A. Brown.
Embellished version of Grave: It. 989:76, 78, It. 998:7, It. 999:
10, It. 1006:4.

93. Violino Principale / Concerto / Del Sig:ʳ Giuseppe Tartini /   It. 935
                                                                           vp, v 1 & 2 obl,
     Allegro   C   :33:/52   vla, bass.
     Grave   3/4   :20:/:21:   22x31cm. 10 st.
     Presto   2/4   48/:112:/134   WM: 83, 75 & 16.
                                                                           Hand A. Brown.
  D. 110.
Embellished version of Grave: It. 989:54, It. 996:4, It. 1001:12.

A minor

94. Concerto / Del Sig:^r Giuseppe Tartini / Violino Principale /

It. 936
vp, vlc obl.
23x32cm. 10 st.
WM: 96 & 97.
Hand L. Brown.

    Allegro C   160
    Grave   3/4 74
    Allegro 2/4 237/capriccio 90/8

D. 111.
Incipit on t. p.
Published as no.1 of Opera prima, Libro secondo (Amsterdam,
Le Cene, ca.1730)

95. Violino Principale / Concerto / Del Sig.^r Giuseppe Tartini /

It. 937
vp, v 1 & 2 obl,
vla, vlc obl.
23x32cm. 10 &
12 st.
WM: 98 & 68.
Hand A. Brown.

    Allegro 3/4 219
    Grave   C   :11:/:11:
    Allegro C 97

D. 112.
Embellished version of Grave: It. 988:58, It. 994:22.

96. No: 51 / Violino Principale / Concerto / Del Sig:^r Giuseppe
Tartini /

It. 938
vp, v 1 & 2 obl,
vla, vlc obl.
23.5x31cm. 8 st.
WM: 62.
Hand A¹. Black.

    Allegro C 93
    Grave   C :8:/:9:
    Allegro C 96

D. 113.
Embellished version of Grave: It. 988:76, It. 995:10, It. 1005:12.

97. Violino Principale / Concerto / Del Sig:^r Giuseppe Tartini /

It. 939
vp, v 1 & 2 obl,
vla, vlc obl.
23x31.5cm. 10 st.
WM: 3 & 68.
Hand A. Brown.

    Allegro C   106
    Adagio 12/8 :6:/:7:
    Allegro 2/4 250

D. 114a bb c.
Embellished version of Adagio: It. 989:62, It. 999:3.

Another copy. Violino Principale / Concerto / Del Sig:^r
Giuseppe Tartini /

It. 940
vp.
23x30cm. 10 st.
WM: unclear.
Hand B¹. Brown.

D. 114a bb c.

98. Violino Principale / Concerto / Del Sig:^r Giuseppe Tartini /   It. 941
vp, v 1 & 2 obl,
vla, bass.
22.5x32cm. 10 st.
WM: 3A.
Hand A. Brown.

B flat major

99. Violino Principale / Concerto / Del Sig:^r Giuseppe Tartini /   It. 942
vp, v 1 & 2 obl,
vla, vlc obl.
22.5x32cm. 10 &
8 st.
WM: 3A & 76.
Hand A. Brown.

D. 116a--.
Allegro 2 is the same as Allegro of Stratico Concerto It. 674.
Capriccio indicated in first movement.

100. [Without title]   It. 943
[vp] v 1 & 2 obl,
vla, vlc obl.
23.5x31cm. 10 st.
WM: unclear & 14A.
Hand B^1. Black.

    Allegro   C   118
    Adagio   C   22
    Allegro assai   3/4   280

D. 118.

101. Violino Principale / Concerto / Del Sig:ʳ Giuseppe Tartini /

      Allegro   C 95
      Andante larghetto 2/4 :20:/20
      Allegro 12/8 12/:22:/28

    D. 119abc.
    Embellished version of Andante larghetto: It.989:38, It.997:18,
    It.1002:7.

> It. 944
> vp, v 1 & 2 obl,
> vla, bass.
> 22x31cm. 10 &
> 8 st.
> WM: 83 & unclear.
> Hand A. Brown.

102. Violino Principale / Concerto / Del Sig:ʳ Giuseppe Tartini /

      Allegro   C 113
      Andante 3/4 :24:/:32:
      Presto 2/4 274

    D. 120.
    Incipit on t.p.
    Embellished version of Andante: It.988:46.

> It. 945
> vp, v 1 & 2 obl.
> vla, bass.
> 22.5x31cm. 10 st.
> WM: 79.
> Hand C. Brown.

Another copy. Violino Principale / Concerto / Del Sig:ʳ
Giuseppe Tartini /

    D. 120.

> It. 946
> vp.
> 23x31.5cm. 10 st.
> WM: 98.
> Hand B. Black.

103. Violino Principale / Concerto / Del Sig:ʳ Giuseppe Tartini /

      Allegro   C :63:/66
      Andante 2/4 :16:/:22:
      Allegro assai 3/4 :72:/78

    D. 121.
    Incipit on t.p.
    Embellished version of Andante: It.989:36, It.997:16.

> It. 947
> vp, v 1 & 2 obl,
> vla, bass.
> 23x31.5cm. 10 st.
> WM: 29.
> Hand H. Brown.

104. Violino Principale / Concerto / Del Sig:ʳ Giuseppe Tartini /

      Allegro   C 70
      Andante   C :8:/10
      Allegro 3/4 133

    D. 122.
    Embellished version of Andante: It.989:16, It.995:5.

> It. 948
> vp, v 1 & 2 obl,
> vla, bass.
> 22x29cm. 10 &
> 8 st.
> WM: 65.
> Hand A. Brown.

105. Violino Principale / Concerto / Del Sig.ʳ Giuseppe Tartini /   It. 949
                                                                      vp, v 1 & 2 obl,
      Allegro   3/4   20/:54:/76   vla, bass.
      Largo   C   :6:/:9:   22.5x31.5cm. 10 st.
      Allegro   C   :23:/41   WM: 4.
                                                                      Hand A. Brown.
   D. 123.
   Embellished version of Largo: It. 989:83, It. 999:16.

B minor

106. No: 48 / Violino Principale / Concerto / Del / Sig:ʳ Giuseppe   It. 950
     Tartini /   vp, v 1 & 2 obl,
                                                                      vla, bass.
      Allegro assai   C   18/:46:/46   22.5x31cm. 8 &
      Larghetto   C   :10:/:10:   10 st.
      Allegro   3/4   :41:/70   WM: 71, 14 & 27.
                                                                      Hand A. Brown.
   D. 125.
   Embellished version of Larghetto: It. 988:86, It. 994:24.

TODESCHINO

   This composer has not been identified.

E flat major

1.   Sonata / a Violino, e Basso / Del Sig:ʳ Todeschino /   It. 951
                                                                      score.
                                                                      22.5x31.5cm. 10 st.
                                                                      WM: 32.
                                                                      Hand H. Brown.

   Incipit on t. p.

Violinist-composer, born in Padua, his real name was Toesca della Castella-monte. He was a member of a family of musicians all associated with the Mannheim orchestra. His father, Alessandro Toeschi, was employed there from about 1740; his brother, Giovanni Battista Toeschi, was a member of the orchestra from 1755 to 1773, and his son, Carlo Teodoro Toeschi, carried on the tradition at Mannheim and Munich. Carlo Giuseppe studied with Johann Stamitz, and entered the Mannheim orchestra in 1752. In 1778 he transferred to the court at Munich, where he remained until his death. He wrote ballet music and much chamber music. Sixty chamber works are listed in Riemann's thematic catalog of the Mannheim composers (DTB, v.16). He also wrote some 63 symphonies.

A major

1.   Concerto / del Sig:[r] Giuseppe Toeschi /

It. 952
vp, v 1 & 2 obl,
vla obl, bass obl.
23.5x32.5cm. 10 st.
WM: 16.
Hand H[2]. Brown.

Listed in Breitkopf supplement, 1768 as V Conc. di Gius. Toeschi [no.] II a Viol. conc. 2 Viol. V. e B.

TOSCHINI, LUIGI

This composer has not been identified.

C minor

1.   Sonata a Tre / Del Sig.[r] Luigi Toschini / Basso /

It. 953
v 1 & 2, bass.
22.5x30.5cm. 10 st.
WM: 67.
Hand A. Brown.

E flat major

2. Sonata a Trê / Del Sig.^r Luigi Toschini / Violino Secondo /

It. 954
v 1 & 2, bass.
22.5x30cm. 10 st.
WM: 63A & 1.
Hand A. Brown.

F major

3. Sonata a Trê / Del Sig.^r Luigi Toschini / Basso /

It. 955
v 1 & 2, bass.
22.5x30.5cm. 10 st.
WM: 1.
Hand A. Brown.

B flat major

4. Sonata a Trê / Del Sig.^r Luigi Toschini / Basso /

It. 956
v 1 & 2, bass.
22.5x30.5cm. 10 st.
WM: 1.
Hand A. Brown.

French violinist-composer, he was a pupil of Tartini, and later conductor of the orchestra of the Elector Clement Augustus at Bonn. When he left that post in 1760 to enter the service of the Prince of Thurn and Taxis at Ratisbon (Regensburg) his successor was Ludwig van Beethoven, the elder, grandfather of the famous composer. Touchemoulin was a noted performer and, according to Schubart, a representative of the French style (Ideen zu einer Ästhetik der Tonkunst, Wien, 1806, p. 189-90). He published six symphonies in Paris as Opus 1 (ca. 1762) and two concertos as Opus 2 (1775).

G major

1. Basso / Sinfonia a Quatro / Del Sig.ʳ Giuseppe Tusmolè /   It. 957
    [Violin 2]   v 2, bass.
                                                                       22.5x31cm. 10 st.
                                                                       WM: 69.
                                                                       Hand A. Brown.

Concertos

A major

1. Violino Principale / Concerto / Del Sig:ʳ Giuseppe Duschmalui   It. 958
    Francese /   vp, v 1 & 2 obl,
                                                                      vla, vlc obl, bass.
                                                                      22x31cm. 10 st.
                                                                      WM: 22 & 63.
                                                                      Hand A. Brown.
                                                                      (bass in Hand B)

Italian composer, born in Venice, best known for his ballets and operas.   He composed about 10 ballets, 20 operas, and several oratorios in the course of his career, which carried him through periods of activity in London, Amsterdam and Lisbon.   The six duettos and six quartets in the Berkeley collection seem to be the only examples of chamber music known by this composer.

1.   Sei Duetti / Del Sig.ʳ Vettor Trento / Violino Primo /   It. 959
                                                                    v 1 & 2.
                        E flat major   23.5x32cm. 10 st.
                                                                    WM: 99.
        I.   Hand AAA. Black.

                        C major

        II.

                        A major

        III.

G minor

IV.

F major

V.

E flat major

VI.

Quartets

1. Quartetti Sei / Del / Sig^r Vittorio Trento / Violino Primo /

It. 960
v 1 & 2, vla, vlc.
23x32.5cm. 10 st.
WM: 46.
Hand NN. Brown.

A major

[1]

D major

[2]

B flat major

3.

F major

4.

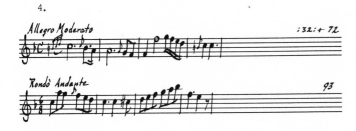

E flat major

5.

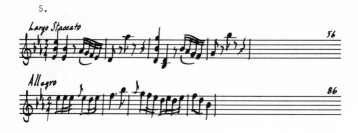

C major

6.

TUSMOLE, GIUSEPPE

   see Touchemoulin, Joseph

VACCHI, FILIPPO

   This composer has not been identified.

D major

1. In D:re 3:º / Concerto / Per Violino Con Stromti. / Del Sig:ʳ
    Filippo Vacchi / Violino Principale /

It. 961
vp, v 1 & 2 conc.
vla, vlc, oboe 1
& 2, horn 1 & 2.
23.5x32.5cm. 10 st.
WM: 49 & 47.
Hand J. Brown.

B flat major

2. In B:fa / Concerto / Per Violino con Stromti: / Del Sig:ʳ
    Filippo Vacchi / Violino Principale /

It. 962
vp, v 1 & 2 conc,
vla, vlc, oboe 1
& 2, horn 1 & 2.
23x32.5cm. 10 st.
WM: 30 & 100.
Hand J. Black.

VAGIANSEL

   see Wagenseil, Georg Christoph

VANHAL, JAN KRTITEL

   see Wanhal, Johann Baptist

VAN MANDER, PIETRO

   see Maldere, Pierre van

Born in Naples, he studied at the Conservatorio di Santa Maria di Loreto in that
city. He established himself as a composer of opera through works performed
in Rome (1756) and Venice (1763). In the latter year he went to London where
he remained for the rest of his life, producing a series of operatic works for the
London stage. He wrote a considerable amount of instrumental music. Sets of
keyboard sonatas with accompanying flute or violin were published in London
and Paris. He also wrote flute quartets.

F major

1.   Trio / Del Sig.ʳ Mattio Vento / Violino Primo /   It. 963
                                                              v 1 & 2, bass.
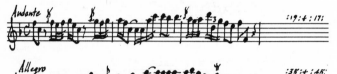
                                                              23x32cm. 10 st.
                                                              WM: 38.
                                                              Hand A. Brown.

Listed in Breitkopf supplement, 1767, as no. 1 of VI Trii di
Wento.

B flat major

2.   Trio del Sig.ʳ Mattio Vento.   It. 964
                                                              v 1 & 2, bass.
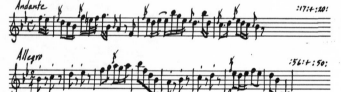
                                                              23x32cm. 10 st.
                                                              WM: 38.
                                                              Hand A. Brown.

Listed in Breitkopf supplement, 1767, as no. 3 of VI Trii di
Wento.

VIMERCATI, GIOVANNI BATTISTA

This musician is unknown. The name, Vimercati, appears in the second edition of Gerber's Lexikon (1814) identified with an Italian composer of the first
half of the 18th century known only through a motet in a manuscript in the library
of J.F. Reichardt. It is also found in the Dictionary of Musicians (London,
1824), which mentions Vimercati as a celebrated performer on the mandoline who
appeared in London during the season of 1824.

A major

1. Sonata a Violino, e Basso / Del Sig:^r Gio: Batta: Vimercati /

It. 965
score.
23x32cm. 10 st.
WM: 73.
Hand B. Brown.

VIOTTI, GIOVANNI BATTISTA, 1755-1824

Violinist-composer, regarded by his contemporaries as the greatest violinist of
his day, he was a pupil of Pugnani. From 1780 to 1782 he made extensive concert tours which took him to Germany, Poland and St. Petersburg. In 1782 he
established himself in Paris where he remained for ten years, chiefly in the service of Marie-Antoinette. The revolution caused him to move to London where
he had great success as a concert performer and leader of the orchestra at the
King's Theatre. His last years, partly in England and partly on the continent,
were marred by a series of unfortunate business ventures as a wine merchant and
as an opera impresario. Viotti was a prolific composer of instrumental music,
much of which is available in modern performing editions.

C major

1. In C: Solfaut / Concerto / Per Violino con Stromti. / Di Monsieur
    Viotti / Violino Principale /

It. 966
vp, v 1 & 2 conc,
vla, vlc conc,
flute 1 & 2, oboe
1 & 2, horn 1 & 2.
23x32cm. 10 st.
WM: 25 & 47.
Hand J. Black.

Listed by Giazotto as no. 32. Premier Concerto ... (Paris,
Sieber, 1782)

D major

2. In D:re 3o / Concerto / Per Violino con Stromti. / Di Monsieur
   Viotti / Violino Principale /

It. 967
vp, v 1 & 2 conc,
vla, vlc conc,
oboe 1 & 2, horn
1 & 2.
23x32cm. 10 st.
WM: 25 & 43.
Hand J. Black.

Listed by Giazotto as no.47. Huitième Concerto. (Paris,
Sieber, 1784)

VODISCHA, VINCISLAO

see Wodiczka, Wenzel

WAGENSEIL, GEORG CHRISTOPH, 1715-1777

Austrian keyboard player and composer, he was born and died in Vienna. He
served as organist to the Dowager Empress Elizabeth Christine and later to the
Empress Maria Theresa, and was a successful composer of opera and church
music.

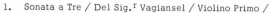

A major

1. Sonata a Tre / Del Sig.ʳ Vagiansel / Violino Primo /

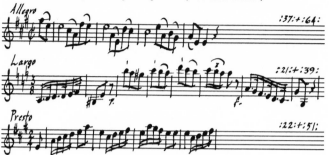

It. 968
v 1 & 2, bass.
23x32cm. 10 st.
WM: 51.
Hand A. Black.

B flat major

2. Sonata a Tre / Del Sig.ʳ Vagiansel / Violino Primo /

It. 969
v 1 & 2, bass.
23x31.5cm. 10 st.
WM: 51.
Hand A. Black.

Listed in Breitkopf supplement, 1762, as no. 3 of IV Sonate a due Violini et Basso di Christ. Wagenseil. Racc. III.

WANHAL, JOHANN BAPTIST (VANHAL, JAN KRTITEL) 1739-1813

Czech composer, he spent most of his life in Vienna. In 1769 he enjoyed two years of travel and study in Italy as the protégé of a Viennese nobleman, Baron Rietsch. He was primarily a composer of instrumental music, and was an important figure in the development of the Viennese symphony. Works by Wanhal were printed in Berlin, Bonn, Hamburg, Lyon, Mainz, Paris and Vienna, and a great many copies survive in manuscript collections in European libraries. Twelve of his string quartets are found in the Berkeley collection.

1. N:º VI / Quartetti / A Due Violini, Violetta, e Violoncello /
    Del Sig:ʳ Giovanni Wanhal / Violino Primo /

It. 970

v 1 & 2, vla, vlc.
23.5x31.5cm. 12 st.
WM: 41 & 30.
Hand YY. Brown.

C major

Listed in Breitkopf supplement, 1782, 3 & 4, under Quattri
intagliati as no. 3 of VI Quattri da Vannhall... Op. XXVI. Paris.

C minor

G major

N:º III.

G minor

N:º IV.

D major

D minor

N:º VI.

Listed in Breitkopf supplement, 1782, 3 & 4, under Quattri
intagliati as no. 2 of VI Quattri da Vannhall... Op. XXVI. Paris.

2.   No: VI / Quartetti / Per due Violini, Violetta / e Basso / Del
     Sig:ᴵ Giovanni Wanhal / Violino Primo /

It. 971
v 1&2, vla, bass.
22x31cm. 10 st.
WM: 101.
Hand PP. Black.

A major

I.

Listed in Breitkopf supplement, 1773, as no. 4 of VI Divert. di
Giov. Vanhall.

B flat major

II.

Listed in Breitkopf supplement, 1773, as no. 6 of VI Divert. di
Giov. Vanhall.

C major

Listed in Breitkopf supplement, 1773, as no. 1 of <u>VI Divert. di Giov. Vanhall</u>.

E major

Listed in Breitkopf supplement, 1773, as no. 2 of <u>VI Divert. di Giov. Vanhall</u>.

F major

Listed in Breitkopf supplement, 1773, as no. 5 of <u>VI Divert. di Giov. Vanhall</u>.

G major

Listed in Breitkopf supplement, 1773, as no. 3 of <u>VI Divert. di Giov. Vanhall</u>.

Bohemian violinist. There are records of him in Paris where, in 1739, he applied for a license to print music. In 1745 he went to Munich as concert master of the Court Chapel, where he remained the rest of his life. Two sets of solo sonatas for violin or flute were published in Paris in 1739, with later issues in London. He also wrote some 35 symphonies which remain in manuscript. It is possible that he was the author of a treatise on violin playing, Instruction pour les Commencants, published in 1757 with later translations into German and Dutch. This work is attributed to T. Wodiczka. In the Berkeley collection this composer is represented by eight violin sonatas, one sinfonia, and three violin concertos.

C major

1. Sonata a Violino, e Basso / Del / Sig:^r Vincislao Vodischa /   It. 972

It. 972
score.
22.5x30cm. 10 st.
WM: 22.
Hand A. Brown.

D major

2. Sonata a Violino, .e Basso / Del / Sig:^r Vincislao Vodischa /   It. 973

It. 973
score.
22x30cm. 10 st.
WM: 22.
Hand A. Brown.

3. Sonata a Violino, e Basso / Del / Sig:^r Vincislao Vodischa /

It. 974
score.
22.5x29.5cm. 10 st.
WM: 53.
Hand A. Brown.

E minor

4. Sonata a Violino, e Basso / Del / Sig:^r Vincislao Vodischa /

It. 975
score.
22.5x30cm. 10 st.
WM: 53.
Hand A. Brown.

F major

5. Sonata a Violino, e Basso / Del / Sig:^r Vincislao Vodischa /

It. 976
score.
22x30cm. 10 st.
WM: 22.
Hand A. Brown.

G major

6.   Sonata a Violino, e Basso / Del / Sig:^r Vincislao Vodischa /

It. 977
score.
22.5x30.5cm. 10 st.
WM: 22.
Hand A. Brown.

7.   Sonata a Violino, e Basso / Del / Sig.^r Vincislao Vodischa /

It. 978
score.
22x30.5cm. 10 st.
WM: 22.
Hand A. Brown.

A major

8.   Sonata a Violino, e Basso / Del / Sig:^r Vincislao Vodischa /

It. 979
score.
23x31cm. 10 st.
WM: 53.
Hand A. Brown.

Quartets

E flat major

1. Violino Primo / Sinfonia / Del Sig:^r Vincislao Vodisca /
    Tedesco /

It. 980
v 1 & 2, vla, bass.
23x31.5cm. 10 st.
WM: 79.
Hand L. Brown.

Concertos

D major

1. Violino Principale / Concerto / Del Sig:^r / Vinceslao Vodischa /

It. 981
vp, v 1 & 2 obl,
vla, vlc obl,
organ (figured)
23x32cm. 10 st.
WM: unclear.
Hand LLL. Brown.

Incipit on t.p.

A major

2. Violino Principale / Concerto / Del / Sig:^{r} Vincislao Vodischa /

It. 982
vp, v 1 & 2 obl,
vla, vlc obl.
22.5x31.5cm. 10 st.
WM: 63A.
Hand A. Brown.

3. Violino Principale / Concerto / Del Sig.^{r} Vencislao Vodisca /

It. 983
vp, v 1 & 2 obl,
[vla, bass]
22.5x31cm. 10 st.
WM: 63A & 73.
Hand A. Brown.

ZANETTI, FRANCESCO, ca. 1740-1783

Italian violinist and opera composer, he was first associated with the Perugia Cathedral as <u>maestro di cappella</u> but left that post about 1770 to devote himself to opera. His most popular work, "Le Lavarandine", was performed in Rome in 1772. He was active in London for a time and most of his instrumental works were published there. These include two sets of trio sonatas, a set of solo sonatas for flute or violin, and six quintets.

C major

1. Terzetto / Del Sig.^r Francesco Zanetti / Violino Primo /

It. 984
v 1 & 2, bass.
23x32cm. 10 st.
WM: 3.
Hand A. Brown.

B flat major

2. Terzetto / Del Sig.^r Francesco Zanetti / Violino Primo /

It. 985
v 1 & 2, bass.
23x32cm. 10 st.
WM: 3.
Hand A. Brown.

ZAVOON, ANTONIO

This musician has not been identified.

C major

1.   Concerto / Del Sig:[r] Antonio Zavoon /

It. 986
[vp] v 1 & 2 obl,
vla, bass.
23x32.5cm. 10 st.
WM: 39.
Hand H[2]. Brown.

Incipit on t. p.

EMBELLISHMENT, EMBELLISHED SLOW MOVEMENTS & CADENZAS

The Berkeley copy of Tartini's treatise on ornamentation is included here with manuscripts in which embellished versions of slow movements are written out in full. The largest groups of these are in the handwritings of the two principal copyists of the collection. For many of Tartini's works, there are identical copies of the same elaborated adagio movements in each of the two handwritings. Three versions (the embellished versions in Hand B for B. E 4, B. G 8 and D. 78) have been traced to originals in the Cappella Antoniana collection, Ms. 1896. The first of these is in Tartini's autograph. Many of the duplicated embellished versions appear to illustrate the exact provisions of the Libro de Regole, with the ornamental figures which illustrate the treatise used in precisely the same ways. Various theories on the origin of these manuscripts are possible, but it is clear that they represent the practices of the Tartini school, if not of Tartini himself.

The Berkeley version of the Libro de Regole is described by David D. Boyden in "The missing manuscript of Tartini's Traité des Agrémens" (In Musical Quarterly 46:315-328. July 1960) and discussed by Erwin Jacobi in his edition of Traité des Agréments de la Musique (Celle, New York, 1961). The embellished manuscripts are treated in detail in Minnie Elmer's unpublished thesis, Tartini's Improvised Ornamentation ... (University of California, 1962).

1.   Libro de regole, ed / Esempi necessari / per ben Suonare / Del Sig[r]. Giuseppe Tartini /

One of two extant Italian versions of the Traité des Agrémens, published in French translation by P. Denis, Paris, 1771.

It. 987
24 leaves (48 p)
23x32cm. 10 st.
WM: 67.
Hand Q. Black.

2. [Embellished versions of slow movements from Tartini concertos   It. 988
    and sonatas: D. 29, B. e 7, B. G 8, B. G 10, B. C 9, B. E 4,   51 leaves (102 p)
    B. E 6, B. A 5, B. A 17, B. F 3, B. D 8, B. c 1, B. g 3, D. 76,   22x31.5cm. 10 st.
    D. 78, D. 69, D. 32, D. 51, D. 38, D. 23, D. 21, D. 120,   WM: 29 & 32.
    D. 87, D. 39, D. 53, D. 96, D. 26, D. 112, B. G 19, D. 4,   Hand B.   Black.
    D. 108, B. g 11, B. B 9, D. 84, B. g 4, D. Anh. VII, D. 113,
    D. 24, D. 103, D. 31, D. 19, D. 125, D. 75, D. 54, D. 20
    (D. 61), D. 66, D. 36, B. G 9.]

3. [Embellished versions of slow movements from Tartini concertos   It. 989
    and sonatas: B. C 12, B. F 8, B. G 18, D. 81, D. 7, D. 101,   48 leaves (96 p)
    D. 22 (D. 28), D. 122, D. 41, D. 79, D. 34, D. 5, D. 83,   23x30.5cm. 10 st.
    D. 35, D. 70, D. 30, D. 33, D. 121, D. 119, D. 104, D. 100,   WM: 98.
    D. 99, D. 44, D. 8, D. 45, D. 11, D. 110, D. 82, D. 80,   Hand B.   Black.
    D. 12, D. 114, (It. 853),   D. 106, D. 107, D. 97, D. 37, D. 27,
    D. 109, D. 109, D. 13, D. 91, D. 123, D. 59, D. 68, D. 23,
    D. 36, D. 6, D. 95.]

4. [Embellished versions of slow movements from Tartini sonata   It. 990
    B. g 3, concerto D. 70, Stratico sonata It. 558 and an un-   2 leaves (4 p)
    identified movement.]   22.5x31cm. 10 st.
                                                                        WM: 29.
                                                                        Hand B.   Brown.

5. [Embellished versions of slow movements from two Tartini   It. 991
    concertos: D. Anh. VII, D. 75 and two sonatas: B. G 18,   2 leaves (4 p)
    B. g 3.]   23x32cm. 10 st.
                                                                        WM: 32.
                                                                        Hand B.   Black.

6. [Embellished versions of slow movements from two Tartini   It. 992
    concertos: D. 81, D. 44, and two sonatas: B. D 6, B. F 4.]   2 leaves (4 p)
                                                                     23x31.5cm. 10 st.
                                                                        WM: 29.
                                                                        Hand B.   Brown.

7. [Embellished version of slow movement from Alberghi concerto   It. 993
    It. 62.]   1 leaf (2 p)
                                                                        23x32cm. 10 st.
                                                                        WM: unclear.
                                                                        Hand B.   Brown.

8. [Embellished versions of slow movements from nine Tartini   It. 994
    sonatas: B. G 19, B. C 12, B. g 11, B. F 8, B. B 9, B. F 3,   22 leaves (44 p)
    B. E 6, B. G 9, B. C 9, and fourteen concertos: D. 31, D. 53,   22.5x31cm. 10 st.
    D. 26, D. 87, D. 112, D. 125, D. 4, D. 96, D. 103, D. 7,   WM: 29, 32, 38
    D. 101, D. 22 (D. 28), D. 19, D. 61.]   & 106.
                                                                        Hands A & A^2.
                                                                        Black.

9. [Embellished versions of slow movements from sixteen Tartini   It. 995
    concertos: D. 53, D. 41, D. 122, D. 36, D. 66, D. 113, D.   14 leaves (28 p)
    Anh. VII, D. 108, D. 31, D. 54, D. 84, D. 79, D. 24, D. 39,   22.5x31.5cm. 10 st.
    D. 93, D. 4, and cadenzas for D. 53, D. 66, D. 24.]   WM: 68 & 3.
                                                                        Hand A.   Brown.

10. [Embellished versions of slow movements from four Tartini
    concertos: D. 99, D. 82, D. 110, D. 12.]

It. 996
4 leaves (8 p)
23.5x32.5cm. 10 st.
WM: 16.
Hand A. Brown.

11. [Embellished versions of slow movements from ten Tartini
    concertos: D. 34, D. 35, D. 70, D. 83, D. 5, D. 30, D. 33,
    D. 121, D. 119, D. 104.]

It. 997
12 leaves (24 p)
23x32.5cm. 10 st.
WM: 68.
Hand A^2. Black.

12. [Embellished versions of slow movements from five Tartini
    concertos: D. 91, D. 23, D. 13, D. 109, D. 27.]

It. 998
4 leaves (8 p)
23x32cm. 10 st.
WM: 68.
Hand A. Brown.

13. [Embellished versions of slow movements from thirteen Tartini
    concertos: D. 95, D. 106, D. 114, D. 59, D. 6, (It. 853),
    D. 68, D. 109, D. 107, D. 97, D. 36, D. 37, D. 123.]

It. 999
8 leaves (16 p)
23.5x32cm. 10 st.
WM: 3.
Hand A. Brown.

14. [Embellished versions of slow movements from six Tartini
    concertos: D. 44, D. 100, D. 8, D. 45, D. 80, D. 11.]

It. 1000
6 leaves (12 p)
23.5x33cm. 10 st.
WM: 35.
Hand A. Black.

15. [Embellished versions of slow movements from seven Tartini
    concertos: D. 31, D. 107, D. 66, D. 42, D. 11, D. 110,
    D. 110.]

It. 1001
8 leaves (16 p)
23.5x32cm. 10 st.
WM: 16.
Hand H. Brown.

16. [Embellished versions of slow movements from two Tartini
    concertos: D. 33, D. 119, and four unidentified works]

It. 1002
4 leaves (8 p)
22.5x33cm. 10 st.
WM: 39.
Hand H. Brown.

17. [Embellished versions of slow movements from Nardini,
    sonata It. 308, Stratico sonatas It. 559, It. 516, It. 473.]

It. 1003
4 leaves (8 p)
23x33cm. 10 st.
WM: unclear.
Hand H. Brown.

18. [Embellished versions of slow movements from two Tartini
    concertos: D. 77, D. 38.]

It. 1004
1 leaf (2 p)
22.5x32.5cm. 10 st.
WM: unclear.
Hand H. Brown.

19. [Embellished versions of slow movements from Alberghi
    concertos It. 50, It. 33, It. 62, Stratico concertos It. 666, It. 667,
    It. 638, It. 651, It. 665, nine Tartini concertos: D. 42, D. 87,
    D. 41, D. 96, D. 108, D. Anh. VII, D. 113, D. 12, D. 70.]

It. 1005
17 leaves (34 p)
28.5x31cm. 10 st.
WM: unclear.
Hand H. Black.

20. [Embellished versions of slow movements from four Tartini
    concertos: D. 97, D. 75, D. 104, D. 109.]

It. 1006
2 leaves (4 p)
23x32.5cm. 10 st.
WM: 3.
Hand H. Brown.

21. [Embellished versions of slow movements from three Stratico
    sonatas It.538, It.419, It.433 and one unidentified work.]

It. 1007
4 leaves (8 p)
22.5x31.5cm. 10 st.
WM: 32.
Hand H. Brown.

22. [Embellished versions of isolated figures]

It. 1008
1 leaf (2 p)
18x31cm. 8 st.
WM: unclear.
Hand H. Black.
(additions in
Hand B)

23. [Embellished versions of slow movements from Stratico
    concertos It.637, It.656, It.655 and sonata It.557.]

It. 1009
4 leaves (8 p)
23x32.5cm. 10 st.
WM: unclear.
Hand H. Black.

24. [Embellished versions of slow movements from Stratico concerto
    It.664, and five Tartini concertos: D. 34, D. 97, D. 24, D. 26,
    D. 30, and one sonata B. B 3.]

It. 1010
4 leaves (8 p)
23x33cm. 10 st.
WM: 3.
Hand H. Brown.

25. [Embellished versions of slow movements from eight Tartini
    concertos: D. 64, D. 45, D. 35, D. 5, D. 78, D. 9, D. 27,
    D. 100.]

It. 1011
4 leaves (8 p)
23x33cm. 10 st.
WM: 3.
Hand H. Brown.

26. [Embellished versions of slow movements from five Tartini
    sonatas: B. c 1, B. g 3, B. d 4, B. F 4, B. g 4, and one
    concerto: D. 70 (fragment)]

It. 1012
6 leaves (12 p)
22.5x30.5cm. 10 st.
WM: unclear.
Hand H. Brown.

27. [Embellished versions of slow movements from two Tartini
    sonatas: B. E 6, B. F 3.]

It. 1013
2 leaves (4 p)
22.5x31.5cm. 10 st.
WM: 32.
Hand H. Brown &
Black. (additions
in an unidentified
hand)

28. [Embellished versions of slow movements from four Tartini
    sonatas: B. D 7, B. F 7, B. e 7, B. c 1.]

It. 1014
2 leaves (4 p)
23x31.5cm. 10 st.
WM: 42.
Hand QQQ. Brown.

29. [Embellished version of Andante from Tartini, Concerto D. 23.]

It. 1015
1 leaf (2 p)
20x29cm. 9 st.
WM: unclear.
Hand: Stratico?
Brown.

30. [Embellished version of Grave, D. 63, and sketch for the arpeggios of Allegro.]
Words and numbers, apparently in Hand B, on leaf 2.

It. 1016
2 leaves (4 p)
22.5x31.5cm. 10 st.
WM: 73.
Autograph: Tartini.
Brown.

31. [Cadenzas in various hands]

a. Cadenze finali.

It. 1017a
6 leaves.
23.5x31cm. 10 st.
WM: 27.
Hand B. Black.

b. Minuetti N?1, e Cadenze N?18.

It. 1017b
2 leaves.
23x31.5cm. 10 st.
WM: 47.
Hand B. Brown.

c. Cadenze.

It. 1017c
1 leaf.
23.5x31cm. 10 st.
WM: unclear.
Hand A. Brown.

d. [Cadenzas]

It. 1017d
2 leaves.
18.5x25.5cm. 10 st.
WM: 102.
Hand: Stratico?
Brown.

e. [Cadenzas]

It. 1017e
1 leaf.
23.5x30.5cm. 10 st.
WM: unclear.
Hand F. Brown.

THEMATIC CATALOGS

1. Mottivi de [105] Concerti [e 82 Sonate] Tartini.

It. 1018a
2 leaves.
23x31.5cm. 10 st.
WM: 76.
Hand A. Brown.

2. [55] Concerti del Sig.^{re} Giuseppe Tartini, [50] Sonate a   <u>It. 1018b</u>
    Violino e Basso del Sig.^{re} Giuseppe Tartini, [16] Concerti del   6 leaves.
    Sig.^{re} Michiele Straticò, [26] Sonate a Violino, e Basso del   23x31cm. 10 st.
    Sig.^{re} Michiele Straticò.   WM: 27.
                                                                               Hand B. Black.

3. [4] Concerti Viotti, [5] Concerti Giernouigh.   <u>It. 1018c</u>
                                                                               1 leaf.
                                                                               23.5x32.5cm. 10 st.
                                                                               WM: 103.
                                                                               Hand RRR. Black.

ANONYMOUS

Sonatas and Keyboard Works

1. Suonate Delle piu Scelte / di Vari e Celebri Maestri / Si Vuole   <u>It. 1019</u>
    ve ne sia anche dell' immortal / Mestrino / in queste sei /   score.
    Groliosa Memoria / Finis Corona Opa /   22.5x32cm. 10 st.
                                                                             WM: 33.
                                                                             Hand U. Brown.

B flat major

[Sonata I.]

D major

Sonata 2da.

At end of Var. 8: "Questa ultima Variazione e Composizione di
Carlino Colpi."

C major

Sonata 3ª.

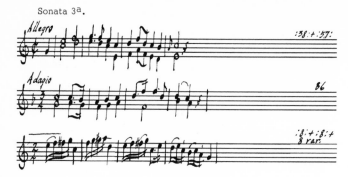

G major

Sonata IV.

Sonata [V]

E flat major

Sonata 6ª.

2. [Collection of organ pieces and sonatas for violin and bass]

It. 1020
score.
22.5x29.5cm. 10 st.
WM: unclear.
Hand SSS. Brown.

G major

Pastorale del Porta.

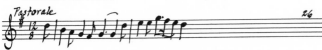

Suonata Pastorale per il Santo Natale.

Includes four sonatas for violin and bass by Pietro Nardini.
Hand TTT. For themes see It. 298 no.1-4.

F major

3. Pastorali / altro in Ffaut Sesto Tuono / altro in Gsolreut 8º
    Tuono /

It. 1021
score.
23x31cm. 12 st.
WM: 79.
Hand UUU. Brown.

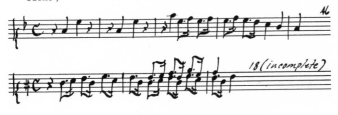

For organ.

C major

4. [Sonata]

:9:+:14:

:54:+:80:

Cantabile   :16:

:38:+:71:

Bass figured.

It. 1022
score.
23x32cm. 10 st.
WM: unclear.
Hand B[1]. Brown.

5. [Sonata]

(incomplete) 12   2d Part   31

Allegro   26+ 35

Tempo di Minuè   :25:+8: (incomplete)

It. 1023
score.
23x31cm. 10 st.
WM: unclear.
Hand PPP. Brown.

D major

6. Suonata / Per Violino e Basso /

Allegro   :20:+:19:

Adagio affetuoso   :17:+:18:

Allegro   :22:+:28:

It. 1024
score.
23x32cm. 10 st.
WM: 76.
Hand KKK. Black.

7. Sonata a Violino e Basso / Del / Sig.ʳ N. N./ [Fragment]   It. 1025

score.
12.5x31cm. 6 st.
WM: unclear.
Hand A. Brown.

Half leaf, with title and first bars of Adagio. Hand A. On t.p.
a series of dance movements in Hand B.

D minor

8. [Sonata fragment]   It. 1026

score.
14x31cm. 7 st.
WM: unclear.
Hand A. Brown.

Half leaf, with first bars of Largo. On verso and on empty
staves dance movements in Hand B.
Former title (erased) "Sonata con Aria del Tasso / del / Sig.
N. N."

E flat major

9. [Sonata]   It. 1027

score.
22.5x30cm. 10 st.
WM: 63A.
Hand A. Brown.

Dance movement in Hand B¹ on empty staves of first leaf.

E major

10. Sonata a Violino, e Basso / Del / Sig:ʳ N. N. /   It. 1028

score.
23.5x31.5cm. 10 st.
WM: 98.
Hand B. Black.

G major

11. Suonata à Violino e Basso /

It. 1029
score.
23.5x32cm. 10 st.
WM: 104.
Hand H^2. Black.

12. [Sonata]

It. 1030
score.
23x32cm. 10 st.
WM: unclear.
Hand H^2. Brown.

On verso: 6 short dance movements in Hand B.

A minor

13. [Sonata fragment]

It. 1031
score.
22.5x30.5cm. 10 st.
WM: unclear.
Hand A. Brown.

B flat major

14. [Sonata fragment]

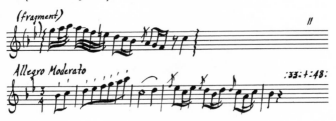

It. 1032
score.
22.5x31.5cm. 10 st.
WM: 105.
Hand DDD. Black.

F major

15. Variazioni a Violino e Basso / [42 variations]

It. 1033
score.
23x31.5cm. 10 st.
WM: 47.
Hand B. Black.

Another copy. [12 variations]

It. 1034
score.
23x32cm. 10 st.
WM: 3.
Hand B. Black.

Duos

D major

1. [Duo]

It. 1035.
v 1 & 2.
22x31cm. 10 st.
WM: 6.
Hand A. Black.

E flat major

It. 1036
v 1 & 2.
23x32cm. 10 st.
WM: 4 & unclear.
Hand CCC. Brown.

2. [Duo]

3. [Duo] IV.

It. 1037
v 1 & 2.
23x32cm. 10 st.
WM: 3A & 36.
Hand A. Brown.

E major

4. [Duo] V.

It. 1038
v 1 & 2.
22.5x32cm. 10 st.
WM: 3 & 36.
Hand A. Brown.

F major

5. [Duo] III.

It. 1039
v 1 & 2.
23x32cm. 10 st.
WM: 3A.
Hand A. Brown.

G major

6. [Duo]

It. 1040
v 1 & 2.
22.5x32cm. 10 st.
WM: 4 & 16.
Hand A. Brown.

A major

7. [Duo] II.

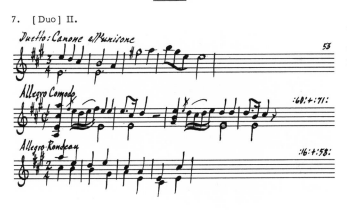

It. 1041
v 1 & 2.
23x31.5cm. 10 st.
WM: 3A.
Hand A. Brown.

Trios

1. Partidura a 3. Sinfonie di D: G: /

G major

No. 1.

It. 1042
score.
23x31cm. 10 st.
WM: 79.
Hand III. Black.

D major

No. 2.

A major

No. 3.

D major

No. 4.

F major

No. 5.

B flat major

No. 6.

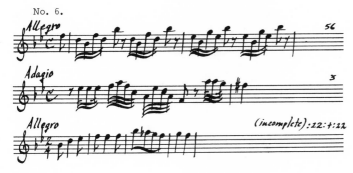

Bass figured.

2. No. VI. / Suonate a due Violini e Basso / del Signor N.N. /
    Basso /

It. 1043
v 1 & 2, bass.
23x31.5cm. 10 st.
WM: 26 & 82.
Hand VVV. Brown.

A major

I.

D major

II.

B flat major

III.

G major

E flat major

C major

G major

3.   Terzetto / Del Sig.ʳ N. N. / Basso /

It. 1044
v 1 & 2, bass.
23.5x32cm. 10 st.
WM: 3.
Hand A. Brown.

D major

4.   Trio Del Sigʳ N. N. / Basso /

It. 1045
v 1 & 2, bass.
23x30cm. 10 st.
WM: 53.
Hand A. Brown.

F major

5.   Trio / Del Sig.ʳ N. N. / Basso /

It. 1046
v 1 & 2, bass.
22x31cm. 10 st.
WM: 4.
Hand A. Brown.

G minor

6.   Trio / Del Sig:[r] N. N. / Basso /

It. 1047
v 1 & 2, bass.
22.5x31cm. 10 st.
WM: 4.
Hand A. Brown.

7.   [Two trios]

It. 1048
v 1 & 2, bass.
(v 2 incomplete)
23x32cm. 10 st.
WM: unclear.
Hand O. Brown.

D major

B flat major

Bass figured. Parts indicated in Hand B[1].

C major

8. [Sonata]

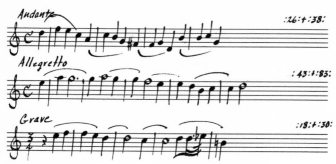

It. 1049
v 1, 2 & 3.
23x32cm. 10 st.
WM: 68.
Hand A. Brown.

Quartets

G major

9. Sinfonia a Quatro / Basso /

It. 1050
v 1 & 2, vla, bass.
23.5x33cm. 10 st.
WM: 3.
Hand A[2]. Brown.

Concertos

D major

10. [Concerto] Violino Principale /

It. 1051
vp, v 1 & 2 conc,
vla, vlc obl,
organ.
22.5x30.5cm. 10 st.
WM: 8.
Hand CC & Alber-
ghi's autograph?
Brown.

At head of title: C. N.

11. [Concerto movement] Violino Primo di Ripieno /

It. 1052
v 1 & 2 rip, vla.
23x32cm. 10 st.
WM: 59.
Hand II. Brown.

A major

12. [Concerto] Violino Principale Cioè / Obligato /

It. 1053
vp, v 1 & 2 conc,
vla, bass, horn
1 & 2.
22.5x30.5cm. 10 st.
WM: 8.
Hand CC & Alber-
ghi's autograph?
Brown.

13. [Nine miscellanous parts and fragments]

It. 1054

1. [16 numbered minuets, probably for keyboard; a group of short
    dances with various titles; bass parts for similar dances.]

It. 1055
score (14 leaves)
19x27cm. 8 st.
WM: 105.
Hand KK. Brown.

2. [Minuets and other dances, principally for 2 violins and bass.]

It. 1056
score (223 leaves)
23x32cm. 10 st.
WM: various.
Hand B. Black.

3. [Minuets and other dances for 2 violins and bass.]

It. 1057
score (51 leaves)
various sizes.
WM: various.
Hands various.
Brown.

4. [Marches for 2 violins and bass.]

It. 1058
score (32 leaves)
23x31.5cm. 10 st.
WM: various.
Hand B. Black.

5. [Minuets. Scores and isolated parts.]

It. 1059
score (12 leaves)
12.5x17cm. 10 st.
WM: various.
Hand B. Black.

6. [119 minuets. Parts.]

It. 1060
v 1 & 2, bass.
23x32cm. 10 st.
WM: various.
Hand B. Black.

7. [Minuets and other dances. Isolated parts.]

It. 1061
parts.
23x31cm. 10 st.
WM: various.
Hand B. Black.

8. Unidentified fragments.

It. 1062
32 leaves.
various sizes.
WM: various.
Hands various.
Brown.

9. Unidentified fragments.

It. 1063
6 leaves.
25x35cm. 10 st.
WM: 66.
Hand B. Black.

10. Balletti [including three sets of variations on <u>La Follia.</u>]

It. 1064
24 leaves.
23.5x30.5cm. 10 st.
WM: 63A & 74.
Hand KK? Brown.

11. [Minuets and other dances, including variations on <u>La Follia,</u>
miscellaneous fragments.]

It. 1065
40 leaves.
various sizes.
WM: various.
Hands various.

VOCAL MANUSCRIPTS & PRINTED MUSIC

As it was constituted when it left Bassano, the collection contained a few vocal manuscripts and a few printed works. The most important of the former are:

Rossini, Gioacchino. Cavatina: Qual tenero diletto nell'inganno felice.
Jommelli, Nicolo. Duetto: La destra ti chiedo. (Hand A)
Alessandrini, Giuseppe. Messa breve. (Bass only)
Anfossi, Pasquale. Sinfonia ... nel Lucio Silla, 1774. (Bass only)

The printed music included three divertimenti and six quintets by Capuzzi; quartets by Haydn, Fodor, Wranizky, and Cambini; trios by Giardini, Lachnith, and Hoffmeister; and duets by Breval, all published in Venice by Antonio Zatta. In addition, there were copies of the first edition of Haydn's six quartets dedicated to the King of Prussia (Vienna, Artaria) and early editions of four Mozart quintets, also Artaria editions. But most interesting is the apparently unique copy of six sonatas by Michele Stratico, published in London by Peter Welcker.

Sei Sonate / a / Violino / e / Violoncello o Clavicembalo / composte dal / Sig^r. MICHELE STRATICO / e dal medmo dedicate / a sua eccellenza / il Sig^r. Girolamo Co: Lion Cavazza / Patrizio Veneto / e Senatore Amplissimo / Opera prima / London / Printed for the Author by Welcker in Gerrard Street St. Ann's Soho / Where may be had just publish'd / Six solos by Sig^r. Chabran, Six by Tartini, and Six by Mazzinghi. /